Praise for
DRAGONA

"Mary Elizabeth Ames masterfully describes her fictional dragon species and subspecies in vivid paleontological, zoological, and ethological detail. These descriptions, together with exceptional graphics and heartwarming short stories, make dragons come alive in the imagination."

—Cheryl Romanek, Former Managing Editor of Creative Services at J. D. Edwards

"A wonderful description of all dragon species. . . . [T]hese wonderful creatures [are] described in such great detail with so much scientific support . . . they become very alive. [The author has] written a most compelling case for their existence!"

—Joni Fritz, Reader

"In Mary Elizabeth Ames's recent book, the author provides the reader with a compelling overview of the different types of dragons that inhabited the world of *Homo transformans*. The past *transformans* stories compel the reader to want to know details about the diversity and complexity of these magnificent creatures. In detail, the author describes parental care, survival skills, and the aloof but cooperative interactions between species. In many respects, she provides some insight into diversity and the need for cooperation that are so challenging for our times."

—Catharine A. Kopac, PhD, DMin, GNP

"As I read Mary Elizabeth Ames's new book, I found myself starting to believe that dragons might really have [existed] or do exist. The author offered such detailed descriptions of the physical and social characteristics of dragons that a sense of connectiveness was established between the world of dragons and myself. . . . The book is a wonderful enhancement for the series of dragon books created by the author."

—S. A. Jarecki, PhD

"The book is written clearly and flows very well. It is wonderfully comprehensive and detailed about dragons. [The] descriptions and explanations are [so] authentic that you may have children believing they now exist. Many times, I had to even remind myself that they aren't real."

—Shelli Mayer, Reader

"I really enjoyed *Dragona*! A precise scientific and concise literary description of . . . dragons."

—Tacey Battley, Reader

Dragona

by Mary Elizabeth Ames

ISBN 979-8-88824-065-6

Published by

köehlerbooks™

3705 Shore Drive
Virginia Beach, VA 23455
800–435–4811
www.koehlerbooks.com

DRAGONA

Mary Elizabeth Ames

VIRGINIA BEACH
CAPE CHARLES

TABLE OF CONTENTS

PREFACE

Dragons and their interactions with humans are integral to the story of a rare species of human that can transform into another species of animal—reversibly and at will—if they have the genes to do so. Throughout the stories of *Homo Transformans*, dragons exert a significant influence on human affairs, including the outcomes of human conflicts.

For those who are intrigued by dragons—especially fire dragons—*Dragona* provides an in-depth review of the natural history of dragon species found in *Homo Transformans: The Origin and Nature of the Species, H'Ilgraith,* and *Raephela*. This handbook builds on and expands the descriptions provided in these novels. It also presents new species not previously encountered and further elucidates the evolution, differentiation, and migration of dragons, which supports their different characteristics.

From a taxonomist's perspective, dragon species are organized into different classifications based on their genetics, morphology, and where they fit into the evolution of animals (table 1). In this schema, dragons are depicted as mammals. Hence, the taxonomy of dragons begins with the subclass *Monotremata*, followed by the superfamily *Dragonidae*—an ancient branch of *Monotremata* that evolved around ninety-five to seventy-five million years ago—and finally focuses on the subfamily *Dragona ignis aflatu*—fire dragons.

From a naturalist's perspective, dragon species are distinguished by their physical characteristics (e.g., size, coloring, capabilities, etc.), and characterized by social behaviors (e.g., hierarchy, communication, parenting, etc.), defenses (e.g., camouflage, combat tactics, dragon fire), predator/prey relationships, and their subsequent interactions with another animal species—humans.

Domain: Eukarya
Kingdom: Animalia
Phylum: Chordata
Class: Mammalia
Subclass: *Monotremata*
Order: Carnivora
Superfamily *Dragonidae*
Subfamily: *Dragona ignis aflatu*
Genus: *Dragonensis*
Species: *Dragonis*

Table 1: Taxonomy of Dragona

Short stories and vignettes thread through the narrative. They provide examples of dragon characteristics and behaviors, including interactions with humans. The graphic artists of EpicMade produced the illustrations that depict the various species found in *Dragona.*

Although the author has attempted to make the content regarding general mammalian biology accurate, any reference to fire-breathing dragons is pure fantasy. Even though biology supports the existence of dragons, to date no animal species has demonstrated the physiologic capability to generate fire. The author has chosen to use the National Library of Medicine citations throughout the book.

Supplemental Notes and Citations

Continental Fragmentation and Separation

During the Mesozoic era, approximately 242–266 million years ago, the supercontinent Pangaea broke up (Vavrek, 2016). By the mid-Cretaceous period, approximately 100 million years ago, the Gondwanaland province of Pangaea had split into five separate continents (Veevers, 2004). The separation and fragmentation of the continents led to increased biodiversity, as different species evolved and adapted to their environment.

Mammalian Subclasses

There are three subclasses of mammals. The subclass *Prototheria* (monotremes) is almost extinct (Jones and Safi, 2011). Monotremes are the oldest species of mammals. They evolved approximately 220–110 million years ago on the supercontinent once known as Pangaea. In reality, only five living species of monotremes remain: one is the duck-bill platypus (Australia), family *Ornithorhynchidae,* and four are the echidna (New Zealand), family *Tachyglossidae.*

Mammals further diverged into the subclass *Metatheria* (marsupials, e.g., kangaroos, koalas) and subsequently into the subclass *Eutheria* (placentals, all other mammals).

Reptilia

Although labeled dragons, the iguana, the bearded dragon, and the Komodo dragon fall under the class *Reptilia* and are identified as lizards. The iguana falls under the family *Iguanidae.* The bearded dragon falls under the family *Agamidae.* The Komodo dragon is a member of the *Varanidae* family.

PROLOGUE

A Wolf-Rayet star, not astronomically far from Earth's backyard, exploded into a massive supernova—*Stella Ignis*—releasing a gamma ray burst that struck Earth. It was a near-extinction-level event. People were driven deep underground, taking with them as many animals and plants and as much technology as they could. Over the next 150 years, human civilization eked out an existence before people dared to emerge above ground.

Meanwhile, a few species of animals—including tardigrades and dragons—were radiation resistant. They had the innate ability to repair genes damaged by radiation. Other species of animals—including humans—that escaped into caves, caverns, deep-water rivers, and oceans survived the gamma ray burst. Still, many that survived the initial blast eventually died from lingering exposure. Yet, not all were lost. Of those that survived, subsequent generations repopulated the land. In the interim, land-based dragons descended from their mountain retreats and resumed roaming Earth as they and the dinosaurs once had.

Prior to *Stella Ignis*, people believed that dragons existed only in mythology. Paleontologists also dismissed the notion that dragons ever existed. There was fossil evidence for dinosaurs, whereas there was none for dragons. When a dragon died, its kinsmen destroyed the body with dragon fire so intense that not even ashes remained.

Furthermore, dragons inhabited relatively extreme environments: high mountain ranges, ocean depths, deep rivers, and subterranean cavern systems. Over thousands of years, their physique had adapted, giving them the ability to blend into their respective environments. Thus, dragon sightings had been extremely rare. When they occurred, people dismissed them as a refraction of sunlight, an unidentified flying object, a figment of imagination, or a hallucination. Post *Stella Ignis*, as humans emerged and resumed occupying the Earth's surface, dragon sightings occurred with much greater frequency and clarity.

Supplemental Notes and Citations

Genes and DNA

Deoxyribonucleic acid (DNA) is the building block of genetic material (figure 1). Genes comprise segments of DNA, which ultimately drive the structure and function of living organisms.

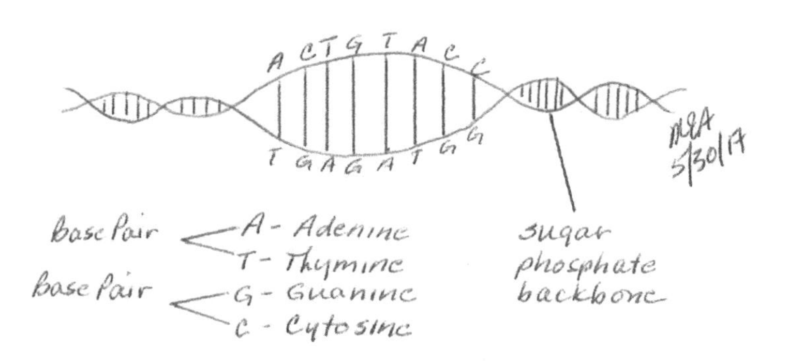

Figure 1: Genes and DNA

DNA Repair

Endonucleases are enzymes that can target and excise specific genes (DNA sequences). Other DNA enzymes (e.g., DNA polymerase) can repair damaged DNA (Ishino and Ishino, 2014). They are used in biogenetics applications to "edit" genes (Paul and Montoya, 2020).

Tardigrades

Tardigrades are small aquatic animals that are highly resistant to gamma rays and other environmental stresses as a result of robust DNA repair mechanisms (Jönsson, 2019).

PRELUDE
There Be Dragons

When looking for a secure place to establish a community, *H. transformans* scouts would become their alternate species to investigate the land. One such scout was a young man who, as a coyote, headed south to explore the southern territory well beyond any areas inhabited by humans. After traveling without seeing any signs of other people or human habitation, he entered the wide expanse of grasslands farther south. Open grasslands offered no place to hide and no protection from the elements. Yet, grains strewn among grasses offered a bounty that could last through winter.

As the coyote explored the region, he came upon creeks and streams with trees lining their banks. This raised the possibility of growing fruit and nut trees that could blend in with native trees—pines, willows, birch, sweet gum, and maple.

Beyond the grasslands farther toward the southwest, he saw a range of mountains rising in the distance. Mountains offered caves, crevasses, and caverns that might harbor people.

This is perfect, he thought. *We can hide in the mountains. Scouts can spot anyone coming into this region long before they see us.*

As the coyote trotted along, an abrupt wind gust arose, blowing the grasses briskly. Suddenly, a shadow appeared overhead. He glimpsed a creature known only in legends. A male red dragon was diving straight at him (illustration 1). The coyote had no chance to flee before being swept off the ground. The dragon swiftly and expertly grasped the coyote with one talon and flew away, carrying its next meal back to the southern mountains.

Illustration 1: Red Dragon Hunting

A Puzzlement

By the time the dragon reached its aery, the coyote was unconscious. As the dragon deposited the coyote in his cave, he saw a chrysalis forming over it. Startled yet curious, the dragon watched as the chrysalis shrouded the body. Not even the dragon's raptor-like vision could penetrate the shroud. He nudged it slightly with his snout and detected movement inside it.

Still curious, the puzzled dragon watched and waited. A short time later, the shroud disintegrated, revealing a human male. Recognizing the species immediately, the dragon grasped the still-unconscious man in his talon and took him back to the same place where the dragon had snatched a coyote.

The human's appearance so far south forebode the arrival of humans in a territory where red dragons ranged. This was a source of consternation for them. Up to this point, they had watched the activity of humans from altitudes that strained the range of human vision. They had spent centuries keeping themselves from being discovered by humans—the only species that might prey on dragons.

Fairytales and Foolishness

Once awake, the young man found himself alone on terra firma. He promptly transformed into a coyote again and raced back to his kinsmen with a tale no one would believe. His report of being snatched up by a dragon and then released was met with considerable skepticism.

"He probably encountered some wild psilocybin and sniffed too much of it," some people whispered.

"Perhaps he suffered sunstroke or became overheated and dehydrated, causing delusions and hallucinations," remarked the more charitable.

In any case, all were certain that there were no such things as dragons. The young man's inability to provide a concrete description augmented their disbelief. Before long, he began to think that he must have hallucinated, if only because he was still alive. In mythology, dragons were almost invariably hostile and deadly. Yet, he remained haunted by the specter of a dragon—real or otherwise.

The Human Factor

After *Stella Ignis*, dragons had had a temporary respite from dodging *Homo sapiens*. They had observed the effects of *Stella Ignis* on human civilization. Humans had gone underground, effectively vanishing off the face of the Earth for well over a century. Subsequently, dragons and other surviving species roamed freely throughout their respective territories until human populations reemerged.

When humans reappeared on the surface, they found that their highly mechanized, sophisticated, and mobile society had virtually disappeared. For all practical purposes, human society had been blasted back into the fourteenth century to resume a largely agrarian lifestyle. Yet, human knowledge had not been lost. Thus, human society advanced briskly despite a lack of modern resources. Once engines could be rebuilt and provide power, advanced technology became available.

During this time, people began reclaiming and recolonizing many territories. In the woodlands to the north, humans built several large settlements. In the south, human settlements remained sparse and widely dispersed. Eventually, explorers discovered passes through the northern mountain range, which allowed them to breach that barrier and enter arctic territory. One pass in particular was open from early summer to early fall. Through this pass, humans established a settlement in the subarctic. Despite harsh winters—or possibly because of them—this settlement was virtually isolated from all other human settlements, including their conflicts, until the spring thaw reopened the pass.

Meanwhile, dragons withdrew into their native habitats—regions that humans found inhospitable. There, they resumed their watch from afar. Over time, humans would hear rumors of an animal that had been relegated to mythology. Most people dismissed the notion of dragons as imaginary and wishful thinking.

A New Species

Over time, dragons noted a developmental change in some humans, occurring after the *Stella Ignis* supernova. *Homo sapiens* was no longer a single species. A second species, *Homo transformans*, had arisen from exposure to gamma radiation. This new species of human could undergo metamorphosis—reliably, reversibly, and at will. They could transform into another species of animal, provided they had the genes to do so.

This new capability created a rift in human society. Initially, people who could transform were shunned as freaks. When word spread that some could transform into an apex predator, a malevolent organization—the Cassius Foundation—began hunting them for the power they possessed. The people who owned the foundation intended to harness this ability to dominate society. Consequently, clashes among human communities increased and spread across many territories.

People who could transform fled into unmapped territories, looking for places where they could live in safety—free from persecution. Many led a migrant's life and were always on the move. Others fled far enough away to disappear and establish communities of their own in remote regions. The first of these communities was the House of H'Aleth. Subsequently, the House of Erwina and the House of Gregor were established.

This rift in human society was hardly the first that dragons had observed. Over the centuries, many disputes had led to armed conflicts. When these occurred, dragons would retreat deep into their habitats to avoid becoming incidental casualties, while still keeping a close watch on all parties—albeit from a safe distance.

Once dragons discovered that humans could transform, this complicated their hunts significantly. In order to avoid interactions with humans, dragons needed to distinguish native animals from transformed humans. It was not long before dragons discerned the difference. Humans had their own scent as did all other species of animals. A human who transformed into an alternate species still carried some human scent as well as that of his alternate species. Dragons quickly picked up on the collage of scents. Once learned, they could readily distinguish a transformed human from a native animal species.

Engagements

Wild animals, including dragons, generally avoided any contact with humans. For dragons, human actions were difficult to predict. They seemed to wax and wane between being peaceful and becoming violent. Hence, dragons made every effort to avoid contact with people unless drawn in by human conflict.

Once humans discovered that dragons were real and not figments of their imagination, most humans were just as eager to avoid dragons. Still, there were instances when sympathetic humans and adult dragons engaged with each other for the benefit of both. This coalesced for the red dragons when an *H. transformans*, who could transform into a lynx and a great horned owl, intervened to save an adolescent red dragon from hunters. Years later, a similar event occurred wherein an old woman and young child freed an injured great gray dragoness from her tormentors.

From these and other similar interactions, a tacit understanding of live and let live developed among some communities of humans and some clans of dragons. Gradually, a rapport developed between them as a result of unintended encounters wherein both parties benefited from the situation. Over time, this evolved into an accord to keep watch for a common enemy that threatened both of them—the Cassius Foundation. To do so, human scouts and dragon sentinels needed to recognize each other. Scouts were not the only humans to enter dragon territories. Bounty and trophy hunters also walked there, searching for any unwary *H. transformans*, a lost dragon egg or chick, or even a hapless dragon. Such treasures would fetch a high price.

A Common Enemy

The Cassius Foundation was determined to achieve total domination over all the territories and everyone and everything in them. To this end, it enlisted bounty hunters to seize people who were *Homo transformans*, to capture native species of powerful animals—especially apex predators—and seize dragon chicks and eggs. Through the misuse of genetic engineering, the foundation modified the genomes of both *Homo transformans* and native species, creating deadly hybrids. Animal hybrids recognized other species as either food or an adversary, including their handlers. If left uncaged or unchained, they would attack almost anything, including a dragon. Thus, they were used to terrorize and subjugate anyone the foundation could reach.

The Cassius Foundation also sought to harness the power and capabilities of a fire dragon. To gain this advantage, it needed the genes of a dragon. Hence, the foundation prized dragon chicks and eggs above all other species and set the bounty high. Eager to receive such tempting rewards, bounty hunters set out to kill or steal dragon offspring.

Dragon aeries were far too high for hunters to reach, so eggs and nestlings were not a target. Instead, hunters targeted any youngster or juvenile that was too young to make fire. Some even tried to kill an adult dragon using catapults, cannons, and arrows. These efforts proved fruitless. If mortally wounded, the dragon would immolate itself, ensuring that no trace of its body would be left—not even its ashes. After a while, most bounty hunters decided that hunting dragons of any age was impractical, unprofitable, and usually lethal.

Supplemental Notes and Citations

Psilocybin is a hallucinogenic compound found in some species of mushrooms (Caronaro, *et al.*, 2016; Madsen, *et al.*, 2019; Tyls, *et al.*, 2014).

Part I
The Rise of Dragons

CHAPTER 1

Of Dinosaurs and Dragons

A New Home

After a long trek across arid scrublands, a herd of weary dragons migrated into a vast plain of grassland, where they dispersed. A young dragoness and her mate were among them. They settled on a place that the dragoness thought suitable for a nest. To camouflage the nest's location, the couple harvested grasses remote from the nest site. They subsequently wove these grasses into and around those growing at their nest site. When the dragoness was satisfied with the nest, she settled into it and laid two eggs. The dragoness remained on the nest, incubating her eggs, while her mate hunted for food. Hadrosaurs were often on the menu.

After six to eight weeks, two chicks emerged from their leathery shells. Initially, the chicks lapped milk secreted by glands on the mother's abdomen. When they began to eat solid food, the dragoness pulled meat from prey to feed her chicks.

Even then, the male continued to do all the hunting. There were many predators that would find dragon chicks a tasty snack. Several carnivorous therapod dinosaurs roamed the grasslands. At five pounds and two feet tall, the *Hesperonychus* could sink into the tall grass of the plains and creep up on its prey. The *Dromaeosaurus*, thirty-five pounds and one and one-half feet tall, was an ambush predator. Its speckled coloring camouflaged it. If the nest were left unattended, these and other predators would raid it for eggs or unfledged chicks.

Fortunately, the dragon chicks grew rapidly. Soon, they were demanding ever-increasing amounts of meat. They largely snubbed token offerings of tree nuts and fruits. Once their scales became tough and leathery, the dragoness moved them to a small copse of trees with dense underbrush, where they were less likely to be spotted by predators. She allowed them to venture forth from the trees as long as they did not stray too far.

Predators

One day, a sharp rumble from the dragoness alerted the chicks to scurry back to the trees. She had spotted a *Velociraptor*—a voracious predator. It was six feet long, weighed eighty pounds, and had serrated teeth with a bite force of 1,600 pounds per square inch. The raptor scanned the terrain, looking for potential prey. Unattended dragon chicks would do nicely, provided it could spot an errant chick or an unprotected nest. Unbeknownst to the raptor, it was not the only predator at hand.

The dragoness nudged her chicks with a deep, soft rumble, admonishing them to watch and remain perfectly still. Ordinarily, the dragoness would have hunted the velociraptor from aloft, catching it by surprise. Since her chicks were not yet fledged, they could not accompany her in flight. So the dragoness also watched and waited until her unwary prey came within range.

When the *Velociraptor* was close enough, the dragoness darted from the trees. The raptor bolted—too late. The much larger dragoness only needed a brief burst of speed before talons brought down her prey (illustration 2). Her powerful jaws crushed its throat as her own serrated teeth sank into it. Seconds later, the struggle was over, and the dragoness called her chicks. Once they started to feed, she voiced a deep, resounding rumble that traveled for miles. She was calling her mate to join in the feast.

Migration of Dinosaurs and Dragons

Some of the earliest descendants of the monotreme line migrated into the land mass that ultimately became South America. Approximately seventy-five million years ago, a narrow isthmus, raised by tectonic activity, provided an avenue whereby many classes and species of animals could move between the South and North American continents. Dinosaurs and dragons were among the species that migrated across this bridge. Descendants of *Monotremata dragonis* crossed into southwestern regions of what is now the United States.

Illustration 2: Red Dragon Mother

Due in part to predatory pressures, many dragons migrated into territories in search of space, suitable climate, and food sources. During their initial colonization of North America, land-based dragons settled in the plains where they nested and reared their offspring. This was not without peril. Dragon eggs and chicks, hidden in nests and burrows, were vulnerable to many predators of that period. Although adults and juveniles could become airborne, chicks could not fly until they were fully fledged.

Furthermore, dragons were not the only apex predator. The *Allosaurus* and *Tyrannosaurus*, among others, competed with dragons for food and dominance. Although dragons were on par with these dinosaurs, the former did not win every contest. Dragons had learned long ago that where there was tinder—grasses, tropical dry forests, dry vegetation—using their fire was not an option. Fire would spread rapidly, engulfing the entire area and endangering all wildlife that could not outrun—or outfly—the fire, including their own chicks and eggs. These pressures eventually drove the dispersion of dragons.

Ancestral Spread of Dragons

Many dragons were primarily land-based. They included montane (mountain) dragons, freshwater aquatic (rivers and lakes) dragons, arboreal (tree-dwelling) dragons, and subterranean (cavern-dwelling) dragons (figure 2). Marine (saltwater) dragons were ocean-faring. One brackish-water specialist in particular traversed both swampland and marine environs.

Ancestral migrations of land-based dragon lineages spread throughout tropical, arid, temperate, and subarctic tundra regions. Initially, they encountered the southern and southwestern mountain ranges. Others migrated farther north to colonize the southern face of the high northern mountain range. Still others migrated even farther to colonize the northern face and subarctic regions.

As a rule, dragons did not migrate seasonally. They were social animals with an established home territory. They did not move from it unless conditions became untenable. Thus, over many generations, environmental conditions triggered changes in physique.

Figure 2.

Biological Tree of

Dragona ignis aflatu

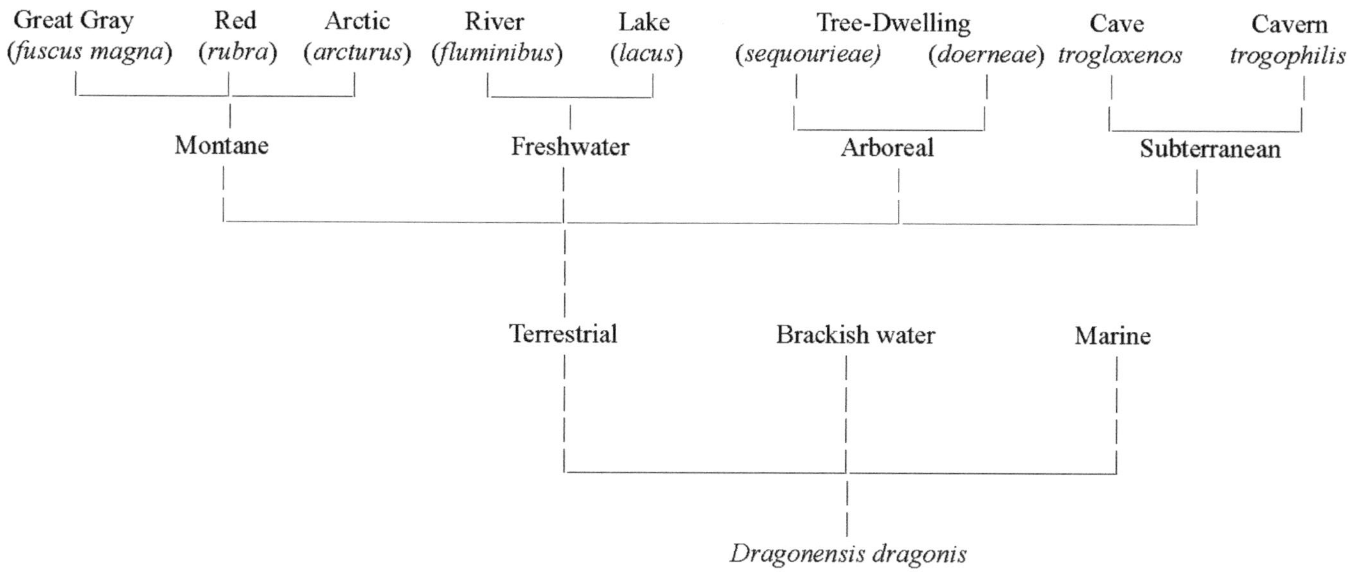

Great Gray (*fuscus magna*)
Red (*rubra*)
Arctic (*arcturus*)
Montane

River (*fluminibus*)
Lake (*lacus*)
Freshwater

Tree-Dwelling (*sequourieae*) (*doerneae*)
Arboreal

Cave *trogloxenos*
Cavern *trogophilis*
Subterranean

Terrestrial
Brackish water
Marine

Dragonensis dragonis

The red dragons (*Dragonis rubra*) adapted to arid and semi-arid regions and settled in the southwestern mountains. They developed reflective scales that deflected sunlight and decreased the influence of the sun's radiation on their body temperature. Their aeries were high, where cooler air and winds also moderated the heat from the sun's rays. Their reddish-brown scales also reflected the myriad of colors seen in the southwestern mountains, which helped to camouflage them.

The great gray dragons (*Dragonis fuscus magna*) migrated into temperate and mountain regions and settled in the northern mountains. Their size helped them withstand the harsh climate in the higher mountain ranges. Those with dark-colored scales had another survival advantage. Unlike *D. rubra*, the gray dragons' scales absorbed ultraviolet radiation from the sun, which warmed their surface scales and kept their bodies warm. Thus, over the ages, the dragons' scales became a gray to charcoal-black color. This coloring also helped them to blend into rocky terrains and be less visible to prey species.

The arctic dragons (*Dragonis arcturus alba*) spread into the subarctic and arctic regions, settling into the northern face of the northern mountain range. Although a land-based dragon, *D. alba* was an excellent swimmer. The relatively thin gray scales on the top of its head, back, and wings absorbed heat from the sun. The almost pure white color on their chest, abdomen, and underneath their wings provided camouflage.

Aquatic dragons (*Dragonis fluminibus* and *lacus*) were species that had adapted to temperate regions with an abundance of rivers and lakes. These environments allowed aquatic species to disappear quickly into deep rivers and lakes that provided an abundant food source.

The blue dragon (*Dragonis odontoceti*) and other ocean-faring dragons were migratory marine monotremes. They traversed the eastern and southern ocean waters. In contrast, the swamp dragon (*Dragonis odontis pristis*) traversed both land and water. It harbored in the brackish waters of a swamp, hunting both on land and in the sea. Hence, it differed from both the purely freshwater, land-based, aquatic dragons and saltwater marine dragons.

The evolutionary origin of aquatic, marine, and brackish dragons is unclear. Without fossil evidence, it is unknown if aquatic dragons branched off from marine dragons to come ashore or vice versa. The *Pristis* suggests that there may have been a bridge between aquatic and marine species with the *Pristis* the sole surviving example of an intermediate species.

Supplemental Notes and Citations

Continental Drift

Approximately 200 million years ago, the supercontinent Pangaea began to break apart to form two smaller continents: Gondwana and Laurasia (Weisbecker and Beck, 2015). Under the influence of continental drift, Laurasia drifted northward. About 145 million years ago, Gondwana began to break up into land masses that would become Antarctica, Australia, New Zealand, Africa, and South America. Similarly, Laurasia also separated to form the European-Asian land mass and the Laurentian land mass (North America and Greenland).

About 105 million years ago, the African continent separated from South America (Davis, *et al.*, 2002; Weisbecker and Beck, 2015). About 65 million years ago, South America drifted northward, and a bridge formed between the North and South American continents (Bacon, *et al.*, 2015; Egbert, *et al.*, 2014; O'Dea, *et al.*, 2016). Maps illustrating continental drift may be found at the United States Geological Survey (USGS) website: https://www.usgs.gov/.

Isthmus of Panama

Originally, the rise of the isthmus was thought to have occurred approximately three million years ago. More recently, evidence suggests it was present 73 million years ago and had settled into its current position about 50 million years ago (Bacon, *et al.*, 2015; O'Dea, *et al.*, 2016).

Ancestral Migration of Mammals

Monotremes are the last remaining members of an ancestral spread of mammals from Gondwana (Weisbecker and Beck, 2015). Fossil evidence of monotremes and other flora and fauna from Gondwana has been found in both South America (Argentina) and North America (Texas) (Flannery, *et al.*, 1995; Weisbecker and Beck, 2015). Descendants of *Monotremata sudamericana* crossed the land bridge into southwestern regions (Davis, *et al.*, 2002; Kielan-Jaworowska, 1992; Weisbecker and Beck, 2015). Eventually, the monotreme line in the Americas became extinct. Only the platypus (one species) and echidna (four species) survive in Australia and New Zealand.

Hadrosaurs

Hadrosaurus was a group of herbivore dinosaurs that inhabited the North American continent during the Cretaceous period (Fiorillo, *et al.*, 2018). They can run approximately thirty to thirty-five miles per hour.

Velociraptor

A Cretaceous dinosaur, the *Velociraptor mongoliensis* was a feathered therapod dinosaur (Turner, *et al.*, 2007).

Viviparous, Oviparous, and Ovoviviparous

In viviparous species, offspring develop within the mother, typically in an amniotic sac. They are carried within the mother's body until she delivers the live offspring. This is the normal process in mammals. In oviparous, offspring develop in eggs that have been hatched. In ovoviviparous species, offspring develop in eggs that have not been hatched. They are carried within the mother's body until she delivers live offspring (Gavrilov-Zimin, 2021).

CHAPTER 2

Dragon Evolution

Ancestry

The monotremes are one of the three lineages of mammals surviving to the present day. They evolved from a common ancestor, the cynodont, which existed about 260 million years ago during the late Jurassic period (table 2). Subsequently, the eutriconodonts evolved and eventually diverged initially into the monotremes (cladogram 1) and subsequently into the marsupial and placental lines (cladogram 2).

Dragona is the first branch off the monotreme line, evolving 95 to 75 million years ago. Thus, dragons are the oldest species of monotremes. *Dragona* is also the crown group representing all dragon species, living or extinct. Over time, they adapted to a wide variety of habitats that ultimately resulted in their divergence into different subspecies of dragons (cladogram 3).

Critical Evolutionary Traits

Approximately 250 million years ago, small shrewlike mammals appeared. They adapted to a wide variety of habitats. One species in particular developed genes (genotype) that coded for an enlarged, robust, and resilient spine. Over evolutionary time, conservation of these genes led to the development of a spine that would support the structure, strength, and power of a dragon.

During the Cretaceous period, dragons developed two paramount characteristics—fire, which distinguishes them from all other mammals, and flight, which they share with only one other mammal. Radiation resistance, longevity, and a powerful immune system are additional traits that supported their resilience. Few other animals share any of these traits.

Table 2. Geologic Timeline

Approximate Timeline (mya*)	Era	Period	Notes
2.6 to present	Cenozoic	Quaternary	
23–2.6		Neogene	Spread of fauna from South America across isthmus of Panama to North America ~3 mya
65–23		Paleogene	
146–65	Mesozoic	Cretaceous	Echidna/Platypus branch of monotremes emerged ~75–50 mya
			Laurentia (North America) separates from Eurasia ~80 mya
			Marsupial lines diverged from placental lines ~90 mya
			Dragona branch of monotremes diverged ~95–75 mya
208–146		Jurassic	Monotremes diverged from therian (marsupial/placental) mammals ~166mya
			Eutriconodonts emerged ~186–163
245–208		Triassic	Pangea begins to separate into Gondwana and Laurasia
			Pangaea formed ~225mya
			Mammaliaforms appeared ~230 mya

286–245	Paleozoic	Permian	Cynodonts diverged from synapsid line ~265–260 mya
360–286		Carboniferous	Synapsid line diverged from Sauropsid line ~310–320 mya
410–360		Devonian	
440–410		Silurian	
505–440		Ordovician	
544–505		Cambrian	
4500–544	Pre-Cambrian		
4500			Approximate time of Earth's formation (4.5 billion years ago)

*Million years ago (mya)

Diversion of Eutriconodonts

Cladogram No. 1

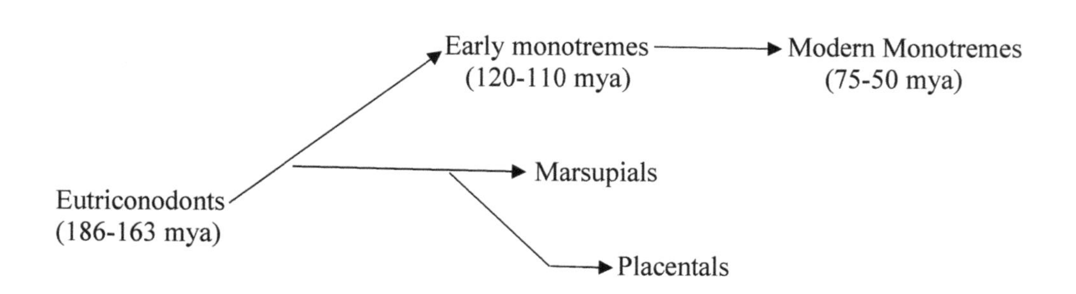

Divergence of Monotremes
Cladogram No. 2

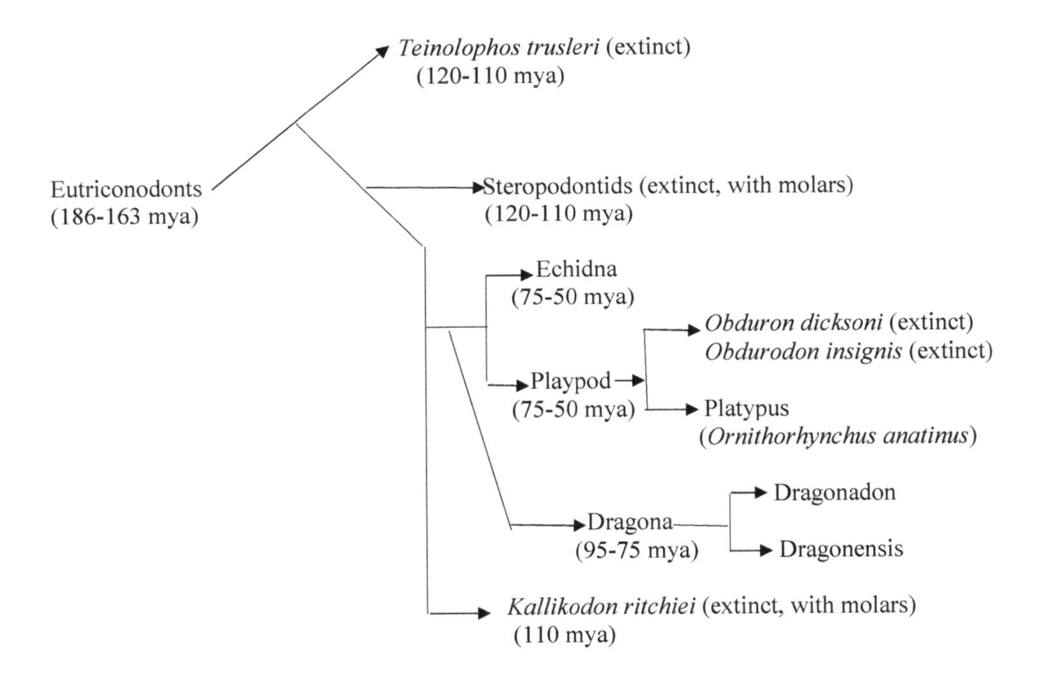

Divergence of Dragonensis

Cladogram No. 3

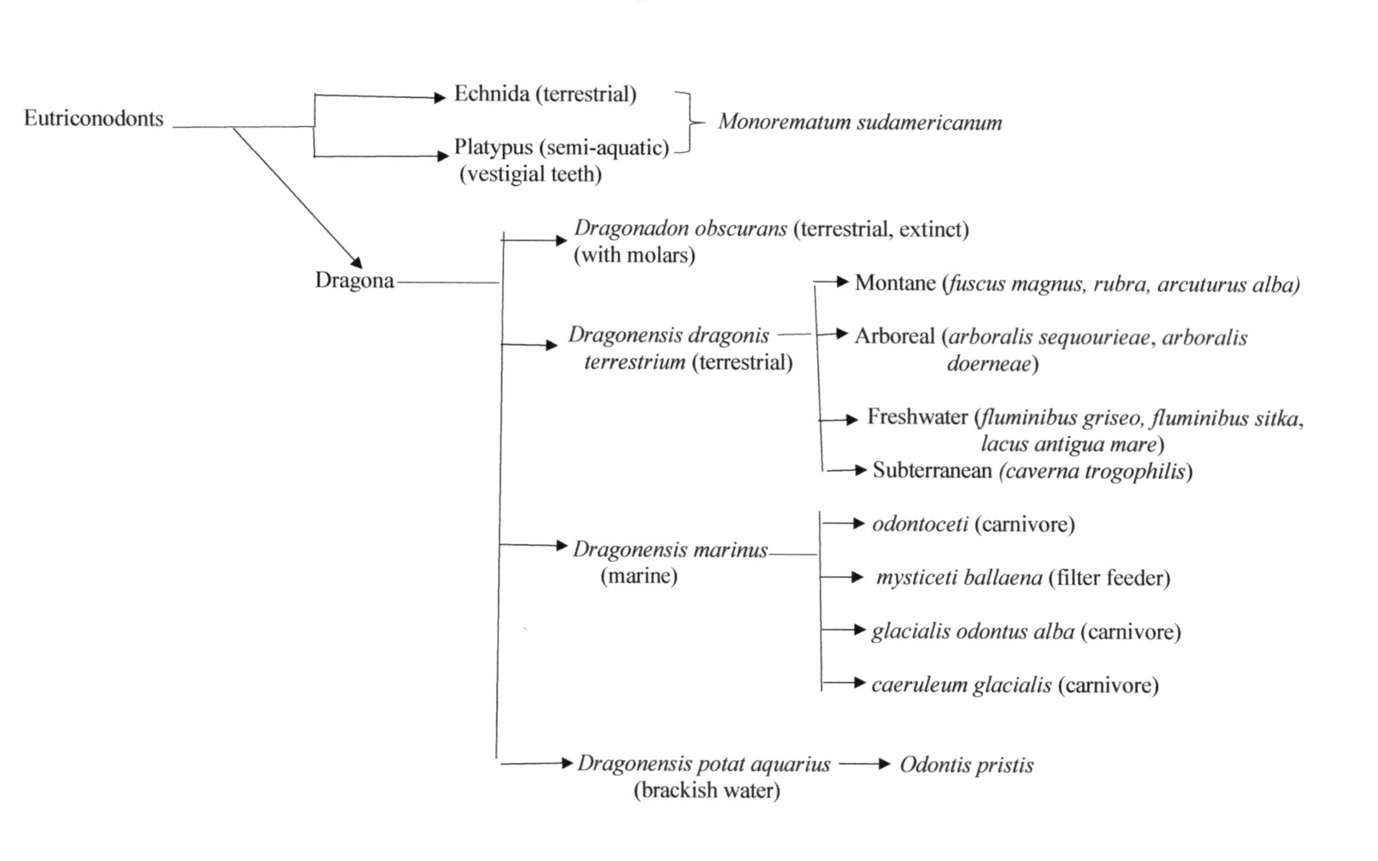
Eutriconodonts
Echnida (terrestrial)
Platypus (semi-aquatic)
(vestigial teeth)
Monorematum sudamericanum
Dragona
Dragonadon obscurans (terrestrial, extinct)
(with molars)
Dragonensis dragonis
terrestrium (terrestrial)
Montane (fuscus magnus, rubra, arcuturus alba)
Arboreal (arboralis sequourieae, arboralis
doerneae)
Freshwater (fluminibus griseo, fluminibus sitka,
lacus antigua mare)
Subterranean (caverna trogophilis)
Dragonensis marinus
(marine)
odontoceti (carnivore)
mysticeti ballaena (filter feeder)
glacialis odontus alba (carnivore)
caeruleum glacialis (carnivore)
Dragonensis potat aquarius
(brackish water)
Odontis pristis

Physical traits that supported powered flight in mammals first appeared in dragons during the late Jurassic to early Cretaceous periods. This led to the divergence of *Dragona* from other monotremes during the early to mid-Cretaceous period. This was followed by the development of powered flight in another mammal—the bat—approximately 64 million years ago.

A genetic quirk triggered the development of a second pair of salivary-like glands adjacent to the existing pair of salivary glands. Alone, the natural substances produced by these secondary glands were inert until mixed with saliva. Initially, when a dragon hissed to intimidate a rival or counter a threat, sparks appeared, scattering into the air. Although initially sparse, the sparks were extremely hot, searing any substance they touched. When the genes supporting this trait were passed on to offspring, the feature developed further. Over generations, the genes that supported the secondary glands and their constituents became ingrained into the dragons' genome. Sparks became a stream of fire, giving dragons an evolutionary advantage against any threat.

Eventually, environmental conditions (epigenetic effects) shaped their distinctive physiques (phenotypes). Although all dragon species have a common ancestor, the development of marine and land-based dragons diverged sharply. Land-based, arboreal, and freshwater aquatic dragons kept the classic dragon phenotype, differing only in size, coloring, and selective capabilities.

Supplemental Notes and Citations

Evolution of Mammals

Approximately 310 million years ago, the sauropsid and the synapsid lines branched. The sauropsids branched again into lines that led to birds and reptiles. The synapsid line began the path to the development of mammals.

The earliest mammals descended from cynodonts, the common ancestor for the three branches of mammals (Deakin, 2017; Kielan-Jaworowska, 1992; Koina, 2006). The evolution of mammals was not linear (Luo, 2007). Multiple additional branches diverged, many of which eventually became extinct, including the descendants of *Monotremata sudamerica*. The eutriconodont branch diversified even further. One of its branches ultimately led to present-day mammals. Approximately 99 percent of all living mammals now belong to the eutherian (placental) subclass (Jones and Safi, 2011).

There are three specific characteristics that distinguish mammals from other classes of animals. Mammals have fur or hair, nurse offspring with milk from mammary glands, and have three ossicles (tiny bones) in the middle ear. Since most mammalian characteristics are seen in soft tissues, there is little fossil evidence. The features that can be observed from fossils include a hinged jaw (detached from the skull), middle ear ossicles (separated from the jaw), and the development of molar teeth (Flannery, 1992; Kielan-Jaworowska, 1992; Lou, 2007).

In general, Mesozoic mammals are thought to be very small—similar in size to a shrew (a carnivore) or a rodent (an omnivore preferring nuts, fruits, and grains). Paleontological evidence suggests that some species may have been larger—large enough to eat a small dinosaur (Hu, *et al.*, 2001).

Genome, Genotype, and Phenotype

The genome represents the total gene complement of an individual organism. Genotype is an individual's overall genetic composition, whether or not it is expressed as an observable characteristic. Phenotype is an individual's observable manifestations (physical characteristics) based on genotype.

Conservation of Genes and Gene Resilience

Genes that provide a survival advantage or are essential to life are passed on (conserved) to subsequent generations (Bergmiller, *et al.*, 2012). Genetic traits that support survival (resilience) in animals include radiation resistance (e.g., tardigrades, *bdelloid rotifers),* longevity (e.g., the Galápagos tortoise), and a powerful immune system (e.g., ostriches, alligators). There may be genes that suppress a dysfunctional gene (van Leeuwen, *et al.*, 2017) or variations in genes that regulate stress responses (Maul, *et al.*, 2020).

Epigenetic Effects

Environmental factors (e.g., diet, climate, etc.) can influence the expression of a gene. Typically, these are biochemical substances (e.g., vitamins) that influence gene functions without altering the gene itself (Ilango, *et al.*, 2020; Zheng, *et al.*, 2021).

Powered Flight

Approximately 50 million years ago, the mammalian ancestors of the modern bat appeared. At that time, they already possessed the physical traits that supported powered flight (Anderson and Ruxton, 2020; Cooper and Tabin, 2008). Other mammals who appear to be capable of flight are actually gliders (e.g., flying squirrels).

Part II
Form and Function

CHAPTER 3
To All Appearances

Escape into Darkness

A young great gray dragoness, a new mother, and her two fledglings were exploring the montane forest abutting the mountain foothills. She was showing her two chicks how to track prey on the ground. Suddenly, the dragoness spotted the approach of several humans armed with bows, arrows, and netting. Hunters! Although the dragoness could easily overpower the hunters, one might still snatch or kill one or both of her chicks.

The dragoness quickly grabbed one chick in her jaws and the other in a talon. This would keep her chicks from taking flight and alerting the hunters. She could not lift off within a dense forest. So she began her climb up a steep, wooded slope into the foothills—somewhat tethered by carrying her two chicks. She had spotted a ledge from which she could lift off. Unfortunately, her dark-gray color betrayed her against the lighter background of the foothills.

Spotted by the hunters, the dragoness could not gain enough speed on the slope to become airborne. With the deep rumble characteristic of her species, she called to any of her clan who might hear her. Struck by multiple arrows, she knew she must find shelter as quickly as possible.

Having noticed a dark shadow on the face of a granite escarpment, the dragoness headed for it. It might be a cave where she could hide her two chicks and confront her attackers. When she reached it, echoes from its walls revealed a shallow cave until they fell away on one side. There, the dragoness found a large opening that led to a complex tectonic cavern system.

With the hunters closing in, the dragoness ventured deep into the cavern, where no light fell. There, she mapped the cavern using echolocation to identify the structures within it. She found a well-concealed nook and tucked her chicks into it. With a soft rumble, she directed them to make no move or sound.

The experienced hunters were not without resources. When the dragoness failed to become airborne, they knew that some of their arrows must have injured it. They also knew that some dragons harbor and nest in caves, so they approached cautiously. From well beyond the cave's perimeter, one hunter gingerly threw a lighted torch into it, then ducked back. The hunters waited. When they received no dragon fire in return, another hunter stepped closer to the cave. Glancing inside, he found it empty. The dragoness had disappeared.

"There must be another cave behind this one," surmised one hunter, adding, "This complicates matters."

"No kidding," replied another hunter sarcastically.

They debated whether or not to pursue.

"The dragoness is wounded. She could be incapacitated," remarked one hunter.

"She's not that wounded!" argued another hunter. "Otherwise, she would not have reached the cave."

So they waited a while longer, debating the risk of death against the benefit of the riches they could demand. After a few hours without any sign of the dragoness, the lure of riches prevailed. Since they had not been attacked, perhaps she was incapacitated after all or even dead. With their torches lit, the hunters warily entered the cave and found the entrance to the cavern. When they crossed over a large entryway, their torches cast many shadows—including that of a dragon.

The dragoness immediately exhaled forcefully, without fire, blowing out their torches. With her chicks at hand, she would use her fire only as a last resort. The hunters found themselves in total darkness. They became disoriented as they turned to scramble back through the entryway. The dragoness suffered no such constraints. With echolocation, she found and targeted them.

Suddenly, one hunter was hurled forcefully against a rock formation. A whip of the dragoness's tail had dispatched him. The remaining hunters quickly realized that the dragoness could see them even though they could not see her. In their desperate scramble to escape, some were crushed when a large stalactite fell upon them, struck by another blow from the dragoness's tail. Others stumbled into a narrow crevasse and plunged to their deaths. Only two hunters got out alive, not lingering to confront the dragoness should she emerge.

Shortly thereafter, hearing no further human sounds, the dragoness retrieved her chicks. Although her wounds were not mortal, they were painful and disabling. She gradually crawled out of the cave. There, she was greeted by members of her clan who had heard her call for aid.

Appearances

Appearances can be misleading. Covered with scales, dragons appear to be members of the *Reptilia* class (illustration 3). They are not. Plates and scales commonly associated with reptiles also appear in mammals. Armadillos are armed with plates, and pangolins have scales composed of keratin. Dragons have similar plates and scales. Although dragons lay eggs and fly, they do not belong to the *Aves* class. Birds have forelimbs that became wings and hind limbs that vary in structure according to whether they walk, perch, or swim.

Dragons have characteristics consistent with mammalian anatomy and physiology. The key physical characteristic that distinguishes them from reptiles is their metabolism. Both dragons and birds are warm-blooded (endothermic). Reptiles are cold-blooded (exothermic). The key physical characteristic that distinguishes dragons from birds is wings that develop and function independently of forelimbs.

Illustration 3: Scales

Characteristics Common to All Dragon Species

All species of dragons feature a protective layer of overlapping plates (gray dragons) or scales (red dragons, arctic dragons, marine dragons) consisting of structural proteins with a bony matrix that protects the underlying skin. Trace amounts of a variety of minerals allow for different shades of color, especially in the scales of the red and arboreal dragons (e.g., iron for red and brown, azurite for blue, malachite for green, etc.).

The skin's topmost layer has a leathery texture, which provides strength and elasticity and is a protective barrier against the environment. The skin is covered by a coat of dark, very fine "downy" hair (lanugo) that cushions the plates and scales to prevent them from rubbing against the skin. Although dragons are endothermic, the lanugo also offers insulation against the harsh, cold winds and temperatures at altitudes encountered in the high mountain regions where dragons live. For all its benefits, sometimes lanugo tickles the skin beneath it.

An Itch in Need of a Scratch

Lanugo is continuously being renewed, so small amounts are shed every day. If it accumulates under scales, it can become itchy. A telltale sign includes vigorous rubbing of scales against the rough surface of a rock face. Most areas of the body can be easily reached while standing on all four legs. Scratching the back is another matter. Dragons have to rear up on their hind legs and move up and down to reach an itchy spot on the back. This is a sight to behold. A dragon can sustain this activity only briefly before needing to stand down.

Physique

Dragons have a head, neck, and body size proportionate to their length. The angular shaped head has a protruding snout. Adult male red dragons sport horns similar to those of the spiral-horned African nyala. All species have upper and lower jaws armed with razor-sharp, serrated teeth, not unlike those of a theropod dinosaur. The large, muscular neck can turn the head almost 190 degrees, side to side.

Males tend to be larger, with a broader chest and back and a larger, thicker skull. Both males and females have hind legs with feet armed with thick, heavy claws. The legs are relatively short and stocky (in proportion to their size) to support their weight when standing upright. The forelegs are longer and slenderer with long talons for gripping and holding prey.

Unlike avian species, dragon talons do not have a ratchet feature. The dragon decides how much power to use in its grip.

Dragons' broad, scalloped wings taper toward the wing tips. Their wings extend from the shoulder—analogous to raptor wings—and are independent appendages separate from the forelegs and hind legs. The skin of the wings features the same leathery (keratinized) outer layer as the rest of the body. The lanugo on dragons' wings is longer, and it both insulates the wings and acts like feathers. Minute muscles in the skin raise and lower the hairs.

The red and gray dragons lack scales and plates on their wings. Hence, in extremely cold weather, these dragons must seek shelter and keep their wings folded tightly against their bodies. In contrast, the arctic dragons have thin, waterproof scales on their wings, allowing them to dive into the frigid waters of the arctic.

Muscular dragon tails taper like the tail of a river otter. The tail is used as a rudder during flight and swimming and for balance while on the ground when standing erect. When standing on all four legs, a dragon can use its tail like a whip. The tail can help dragons tread shallow water as well. Unlike the arctic dragon, red and gray dragons are not known for their swimming skills. Hence, they do not land in deep water—at least not by choice.

Supplemental Notes and Citations

Plates and Scales

Plates are comprised of dermal bone and horn, whereas scales are made of keratin (Chen, *et al.* 2011; Yang, *et al.*, 2013). The skin's top layer (stratum corneum) contains keratinocytes, epidermal cells that produce keratin. Keratin is a fibrous, structural protein that provides a framework for tissues and is insoluble in water (Wang, *et al.*, 2016). It acts as a barrier against the environment, protecting the outer layer of skin. It is also a component of hair, feathers, nails, horns, and hoofs.

Collagen, a fibrous protein in connective tissue, provides structural support and strength. The bony matrix provides a framework that supports mineral deposits (e.g., calcium phosphate, calcium carbonate) enmeshed with collagen fibers. The armadillo's thick shell of plates cover its head and body (Zho and Tang, 2020), whereas the pangolin is the only mammal completely covered in scales (Choo, *et al.*, 2016).

Endothermic versus Exothermic

Birds and mammals produce and control their own body heat via internal metabolic activity (endothermic). Reptiles cannot control their body temperature and are subject to ambient temperatures in their environment (exothermic).

Skin

The epidermis is the outermost layer of skin. It comprises dead keratin cells (keratinocytes). These protective cells thicken the skin, which serves as a first line of defense against environmental threats.

Lanugo is a layer of fine, soft hair covering the body of a human fetus after about sixteen weeks' gestation. Although usually shed before birth, lanugo may still be seen in newborns.

Arrector pili muscles are minute muscles in hair follicles embedded deeper in the skin (Simandl, 2009). When they contract, hair is raised upward. With the scant amount of body hair in humans, their actions may go unnoticed.

Talons

The power in an avian raptor's talons (e.g., eagle, hawk, owl) is a ratchet system which locks the grip (Einoder and Richardson A, 2006). This power ranges from 300 to 500 pounds of force per square inch, depending on the species.

CHAPTER 4
Fire and Flight

A Near Miss

Adolescent dragons like to stretch their wings and take flight. By engaging in a variety of aerial feats, they develop the skills they need to capture prey and defend their territory. They also like to challenge each other to see which one can fly faster and reach the highest altitude. Last but not least, they engage in aerial acrobatics, including mock fights. The latter could be deadly.

In the aeries of the great gray dragons, two boisterous adolescent males decided to test their skills by parrying each other's moves as if they were in an aerial battle. Each one attempted to best the other by using various flight maneuvers. Speed and agility were essential as wing beats, tails, and talons were put into play.

They were sparing at about 12,000 feet when, suddenly, they could not separate from each other. Their talons had become entwined, caused by twisting aerial maneuvers. They began to tumble over each other in a free fall. Instinctively, they tightened their grip as they would in a real battle. In desperation, one of them issued multiple bursts of fire into open air. It was a distress signal. To their good fortune, an adult dragon spotted the scattered bursts and saw the two adolescents plummeting toward a mountain crag.

A powerful male, the dragon reached the two adolescents in plenty of time to shove them away from the precipice and slow their descent. Once the pair landed unceremoniously on the ground, the adult waited until the two figured out how to separate their talons. It was hardly the first time this sort of thing had happened. Finally, the youngsters detached themselves and stood up, whereupon the adult promptly whomped both of them with his tail.

Illustration 4: Dragon Fire

Dragon Fire

Although the ability to produce dragon fire is a genetic trait, chicks and juveniles cannot generate fire (illustration 4). This capability begins to emerge in adolescence; however, they are still too young to use it effectively and safely. The ability to control and target fire is not instinctive. It must be well practiced in high mountain locations well above the tree line and where little or no natural vegetation grows. Adolescents must learn how to start, stop, and target their fire accurately with sufficient power to sustain it. They cannot become fully independent as young adults until they have mastered control over their fire.

Two pairs of glands—an incendiary and a salivary gland—are the source of dragon fire. The incendiary gland is not fully developed until an adolescent is at least three years old, and most are four to five years old. Adults supervise and guide adolescents as they develop proficiency in targeting their fire, which begins with aiming at large stationary granite boulders until adolescents can achieve a steady stream of fire. Gradually, they progress to smaller rocks and, ultimately, to stones tumbling down the mountainside. Their power increases as they became young adults and, finally, fully grown adults.

Dragons' reputation of "fire-breathing" is a misconception. Dragon fire is not generated by breathing. The incendiary and salivary glands are located adjacent to each other and toward the back of a dragon's throat—one pair on each side. Dragon fire results from a mixture of compounds secreted by these glands. One member of the pair, the incendiary gland, contains a mixture of carbon and hydrogen (a hydrocarbon), a mixture of sulfur and oxygen (sulfur trioxide), and nitrogen—all natural compounds. The other member of the pair, the salivary gland, contains water (99 percent), electrolytes (including sodium, potassium, magnesium, and phosphate), and other constituents. The combined secretions from these glands produce the dragon's fire.

A duct from each gland opens in the lower jaw toward the front of a dragon's mouth. The salivary glands contract independently of the incendiary glands in the presence of food or the scent of food. The incendiary glands may be triggered by adrenalin or by mechanical pressure (e.g., a Valsalva maneuver).

When both glands contract simultaneously and expel their contents, the sulfur trioxide reacts explosively with the water in the saliva to ignite the hydrocarbons. The dragon is already breathing out (exhaling) forcefully when this reaction takes place. When the nitrogen in exhaled air (75 percent of exhaled air) combines with oxygen (to form dinitrogen trioxide), its explosive nature sustains the reaction for as long as the dragon exhales. Most of the components of the incendiary gland require substances that must be produced by the gland via some physiologic mechanism. Thus, the supply of these mixtures can be exhausted faster than they can be replaced.

Both males and females can produce fire. They can spew fire while in flight and on the ground, including while standing upright on their hind legs. This allows dragons to use their most effective weapon with maximum flexibility. Dragon fire can reach twenty-five to forty feet, depending upon the species and gender. Males have a larger chest and lungs, so they can exhale more forcefully than females. The temperature of their fire ranges from 1,600–2,200 degrees Fahrenheit (roughly equivalent to a blast furnace).

Dragon "breath" is distinct from normal breathing and dragon fire. It consists of exhaled aerosolized secretions from the incendiary gland alone. Its golden hue is due to the sulfur contained within it. Dragons will exhale these secretions forcefully to suppress a threat without fire.

Hearth and Home

During the coldest months of winter, great gray dragons harbor deep inside their mountain retreats. Winter temperatures stay below freezing, and gale force winds often prevail. Fully grown dragons would die if exposed to these conditions for long. Their lanugo is not thick enough to keep them warm, and their wings stiffen in the cold.

One winter day, an adult dragon set out on a hunting trip during heavy weather. His family had been trapped in a cave by a blizzard, which was finally subsiding. Once her mate departed, the dragoness carefully harnessed her fire to keep the walls of the cave and outer passageway warm. She had to conserve her remaining fire, using it sparingly to keep the cave just warm enough to prevent shivering in her chicks.

Meanwhile, her mate executed a rapid descent into the montane forest below. He used bursts of dragon fire to warm his descent. He had to conserve his fire as well. With the materials required for dragon fire in limited supply, he would need enough to return home. In the white landscape of the forest below, he quickly spotted the dark-brown coat of a bull moose. Its head was down, intent upon finding grasses beneath deep snow. Shortly thereafter, the dragon returned to his aery with food for his family.

Dragon Flight

There are only two species of mammals capable of powered flight: bats and dragons. The configuration of a dragon wing is similar to that of the bat. Unlike the bat, however, dragon wings are not an adaptation of the forelegs. They are separate appendages adapted for flight, leaving the dragon's forelegs free. Although dragon skin offers some degree of weatherproofing against rain, lanugo does not. This limits the conditions under which land-based dragons can fly.

Land-based dragons prefer to launch into flight from a high cliff face or escarpment. An adult male great gray dragon's size makes lifting off from the ground problematic. It often requires a running start with wings fully extended, lumbering to gain speed. The ground trembles with each stride. When present, a tailwind facilitates liftoff. Adult female great gray dragons and arctic dragons can lift off from a standing position; however, it is hard to do. They, too, prefer a running start. In contrast, red dragons, with their slighter build, can lift off directly from the ground with relative ease.

Freshwater aquatic and arboreal dragons also have slight builds and can lift off easily from any location. Arboreal dragons prefer launching from treetops. River dragons prefer to launch directly out of rapidly flowing river waters. Larger freshwater lake and brackish-water swamp dragons must take off from land.

Marine dragons cannot fly. Through evolution, their wings adapted to serve as fins while maintaining their power to propel their massive bodies rapidly through ocean waters. Their fins can even propel the dragon almost completely out of the water in a breach.

Practice Makes Perfect

Parents and other closely related adults monitor and protect fledglings while they attempt to become airborne. Fledgling chicks must be able to sustain short flights and clear at least twenty-four feet above ground. Once fledglings achieve this developmental stage, they are juveniles. Experienced mature siblings and other adult relatives share the duties of proctoring and guiding juveniles as they develop their flying skills. In the process, they are taught how to cope with factors affecting their flight: changes in their physique as they grow larger and heavier; environmental factors such as wind and weather; types of terrain (e.g., mountains, forests, plains); and encounters with other aerial species, including their own. Once juveniles master most flight conditions, they become adolescents with greater independence and less oversight.

Once adolescents demonstrate proficiency in performing required skills—along with a modicum of prudence in using them—they are allowed to range without adult supervision. Even so, adults keep a sharp eye and sensitive ear out for rambunctious offspring. Oversight from a distance remains since young adults are not fully mature and have limited experience beyond their aeries.

Flight Speed

Depending upon the species, most land-based dragons can reach a soaring speed of 150 to 220 miles per hour with diving speeds of 200 to 300 miles per hour. Mountain dragons, which are acclimated to very high altitudes, can soar at altitudes over 18,000 feet. On the ground, dragons can run from fifteen to twenty-five miles per hour, depending on the species. As a general rule, the lighter female dragons can outpace males on the ground.

Arboreal dragons have a soaring speed of 180 to 220 miles per hour and a diving speed of 275 to 300 miles per hour. Their flight speed exceeds any other dragon species. They are the dragon equivalent of a falcon in both agility and speed.

CHAPTER 5
A Quarry's Scent

The Hunt

A young arboreal dragoness had taken flight to find food for her extended family. She lived in a copse of sequoia trees with several other families related to her. The dragonesses had formed a crèche for their chicks. Given the number of youngsters to watch as they scrambled around, only one adult at a time left the nursery to hunt.

With so many mouths to feed, including adults and juveniles, the dragoness was searching for a large, substantial adult mammal—preferably a deer, bear, or bighorn sheep. It was late fall, when many smaller animals had already gone underground or migrated south for the coming winter. The salmon run up a local river had already passed, so bears were no longer readily available. Moose and elk were migrating south, and mountain cougars were following them. Turkeys and several species of owl overwintered; however, they provided little more than a mouthful of feathers. Deer and bighorn mountain sheep were the main entrées on a dragon's menu during winter months.

The dragoness scouted a dense forest from aloft. Tree leaves had turned varying shades of red and yellow and were already littering the forest floor. Evergreen fir trees were interspersed among them, providing a touch of green. Visibility below the canopy was poor. Yet the dragoness readily spotted movement on the ground. To her delight, a very large bear was slowly weaving its way through the woods. It had spotted a moose nibbling on brush and tree twigs at the edge of a small glade. The bear was stalking it from upwind, unaware that it, too, was being targeted.

Although the dragoness had spotted both of them, she chose to prey on the bear. As the larger of the two animals, it would provide the most meat. Since the trees were too thick for an aerial dive, the dragoness could not yet launch her attack. She needed more room among the trees or a break in them to snatch this bountiful meal for her family. So she remained aloft, staying out of her quarry's visual range.

Suddenly, the bear broke into a run, bursting from the woods. The moose reacted immediately and bolted away. Both species could achieve speeds of up to thirty-five miles per hour. Yet, neither was a match for an arboreal raptor that can dive at 275–300 miles per hour.

The dragoness quickly grasped the bear with both talons. She was lifting it off the ground when she abruptly dropped it into the glade. She turned around sharply and landed nearby. Meanwhile, the moose had long departed.

The dragoness had recognized immediately that her prey was not a native bear. Its scent alone declared it a hybrid. Its bizarre physical features further revealed it was a genetically engineered creature, designed to terrorize and kill anything within its reach (illustration 5).

Her hunt spoiled, the dragoness picked up the carcass and took it to a rocky crag that had no vegetation. There, she torched its body with her fire until nothing was left—not even ashes.

The Common Senses: Vision, Hearing, Smell, and Touch

Dragons have the long-distance vision of a raptor and superlative visual acuity. In open terrain, they can pinpoint movement nearly two miles away. In wooded areas, their visual acuity relies heavily on the disturbance of underbrush by animals moving through the forest. Their eyes are positioned on either side of the face to allow for stereoscopic vision. Given their neck's 190-degree range of motion, they have broad peripheral vision. They can see behind either shoulder; however, they cannot see anything directly behind their back.

Dragons also have exquisite hearing and can identify the location of a specific sound. Consistent with mammalian anatomy, dragons have an auditory canal on each side of their head that leads to the middle ear, where an eardrum (tympanic membrane) and three small bones (ossicles) transmit sound. Unlike most mammalian species, dragons do not have visible outer ears to collect sound and direct it into the auditory canal. Hence, they may not detect sound as quickly as other mammalian species.

Illustration 5: Ursuscro

A dragon's sense of smell is comparable to those of other mammalian species. Once they detect an odor of interest, they promptly identify the direction where the scent is strongest, enabling them to identify the source quickly by sight.

Although dragon talons are retractable, they do not use their forelimbs to touch unless they need to scratch. Instead, dragons use their muzzle to caress and stroke each other and nuzzle their chicks. They will rub their heads together as a sign of affection and to greet a clan or family member.

Taste and Nutrition

Officially, dragons are omnivores. Land-based dragons will consume fruits and nuts; however, they prefer a predominantly meat diet. Almost any native species of animal is prey for a dragon. Yet, many species are particular in what they eat. Land-based dragons prefer adult male mammals—deer, bears, moose, and other large species—given the amount of meat they provide. In lieu thereof, they will hunt smaller species—wolves, cougars, river otters, and others. They rarely hunt other classes of animals. Birds have too little flesh and too many feathers.

The montane dragons dislike the taste of reptiles and will only eat one species of fish—salmon. Salmon is an acquired taste for mountain dragons. During seasonal salmon runs, bears converge along the rivers and streams where salmon spawn. Dragons know this and will hunt for bears along these waterways. If a dragon's hunt is successful, it is obliged to eat any salmon the bear has eaten. Arctic dragons feed predominantly on aquatic and marine mammals and fish as well as arctic land mammals.

Marine dragons will feed on ocean-faring species of mammal and fish. Brackish-water dragons are less particular. They will feed on other mammals, freshwater fish, crustaceans, and amphibians. Aquatic (freshwater rivers and lakes) and arboreal dragons are not so persnickety. They will eat almost anything. Regardless of habitat, dragons do not graze on vegetation or eat insects.

Pungent Prey

A novice dragoness was accompanying her mother on a hunting foray when she heard splashing in a nearby stream. She decided to investigate the activity on her own. As she neared the stream, her raptor-like vision detected rapidly moving objects in the water. As she drew closer to the edge of the stream, she could see creatures she had not previously encountered—trout. Although fish had not been a menu item in her past, perhaps they were edible.

After watching the wiggly creatures swimming past her, the young dragoness stepped into the stream to catch one. This was easier said than done. Multiple attempts to snatch a trout proved futile. They were too fast, too slippery, and too nimble. She was about to abandon the effort when a trout floated toward her. Unaware that this trout was dead, the young dragoness easily caught the fish in her mouth. As she sank her razor-sharp teeth into its flesh, a putrid odor permeated her mouth and nose. She quickly dropped the fish and backed away from it. Trout was off the menu.

Forbidden Fare

With the exception of subterranean dragons, other species of dragons do not eat carrion unless no other food source is available. The odor of decaying flesh is distasteful and considered inedible. Subterranean dragons have little choice. The opportunity to eat fresh meat is rare. As a result, they are the only species of dragons to eat insects, fungi, and carrion along with anything else that wanders or falls into their caverns.

Dragons do not eat other dragons, not even those they defeat in battle. They destroy the dead dragon by fire to prevent any other species from feeding on it. Dragons consider genetically-altered hybrid animals an abomination and do not feed on them. They know that a malicious community of humans has created deranged and extremely violent creatures that would not hesitate to attack anything in their path—even a dragon. If attacked by one, a dragon would kill it and destroy the carcass by fire.

Land-based dragons learned to recognize a transformed *H. transformans* by the latter's scent and typically avoided contact with them. Nevertheless, a scout conducting surveillance as his or her alternate species had to be wary. Many alternate species were on a dragon's menu.

Equilibrium and Balance

Mountain dragons often settle on the precipice of a mountain crag while arboreal dragons perch on the limbs of sequoias. Both may be dislodged by tremors in the earth or gale force winds, yet neither teeter or fall. Dragons have exquisite positional sense (proprioception) and readily correct for changes in physical orientation. In an earthquake, they simply take flight, toting any unfledged chicks with them. In a gale, arboreal dragons use their powerful talons to grip the branches of the tree harboring them. They also wrap their tail around the trunk of the tree while tucking youngsters under their wings.

Special Senses: Echolocation, Electroreception

Echolocation in land-based dragons developed as an adaptation to living in caves and caverns with little or no light. These species emit infrasonic rumbles to create vibrations that reflect off objects, allowing dragons to traverse through complex caves and caverns in total darkness.

Echolocation in marine and aquatic dragons diverged from echolocation in land-based dragons. Marine species hunt underwater. They emit ultrasonic clicks and receive sounds that reflect off an object, revealing its shape, size, and other characteristics.

Similar to the platypus, aquatic dragons (e.g., river dragons) use electroreception to locate and target their prey. They can detect an electric field and determine the direction an animal is headed. Thus, both aquatic and marine dragons can execute a precision dive to capture their intended prey.

Supplemental Notes and Citations

Smell

The olfactory nerve has receptors sensitive to odors. Among mammals, humans have far fewer smell receptors—numbering in the hundreds—

than do most other mammals with receptors numbering in the thousands (Renaldi, 2007). Despite this discrepancy, humans can smell thousands of different odors.

Hearing

The tympanic membrane (ear drum) is a thin membrane that vibrates freely when sound waves strike it. In turn, the membrane strikes the ossicles (malleus, incus, and stapes). Their vibrations transmit nerve impulses to the brain for processing and interpretation. In *H. sapiens*, the temporal lobe (Wernicke's area) of the brain receives and processes the impulses from the auditory nerve and forwards them to other areas of the brain for interpretation.

Proprioception

Proprioception is the inherent ability to perceive one's position in space whether still or moving. Sensors in muscles and joints and sensors in the inner ear send signals to the cerebellum (Han, *et al.*, 2016). The cerebellum integrates this information, allowing one to adjust for changes in position and movement.

Echolocation

Echolocation is the ability to perceive objects in the environment by sound waves. Bats and dolphins are the species most commonly associated with echolocation. They emit ultrasonic signals that reflect (echo) off objects, including their prey (Au and Simmons, 2007; Lambert, *et al.*, 2017; Thaler, *et al.*, 2010). Through echolocation, animals can determine the size, shape, and location of an object and can track the movements of their prey.

Cadherin 23, a key gene in the development of echolocation, is one of three auditory genes contributing to echolocation in bats and dolphins (Lambert, *et al.*, 2017). It is also a key auditory and vestibular gene in humans. Usher syndrome type I is a genetic disorder in humans associated with mutations of the cadherin 23 gene (Lambert, *et al.*, 2017). It is characterized by blindness, deafness, and poor balance.

Electroreceptivity in Mammals

Electroreception is the detection of electric fields, usually caused by biologic activity: e.g., muscle contractions (Czech-Damal, *et al.*, 2013). The duck-billed platypus is the only surviving monotreme with electroreceptivity in its bill (Manger and Pedigrew, 1995). The platypus's bill is its primary sensory organ, allowing the animal to find its prey underwater with its eyes, ears, and nostrils closed. Dolphins, a marine mammal, also possess electroreceptivity

CHAPTER 6
Decision-Making

A Poor Decision

A juvenile dragon decided to embark independently on an exploratory mission. He wanted to investigate a dense woodland forest that abutted the foothills of his mountain. The sounds emanating from the forest were intriguing, and he was eager to practice his hunting skills. He had mastered flight; however, he had not yet mastered effective fire.

Even so, the young dragon felt confident. He had never been attacked by a predator—and failed to factor in the reason. An adult dragon had always been nearby, a guarantee that no predator would approach. So the young dragon took flight to go on an adventure without his primary means of self-defense.

The young dragon was already familiar with wooded terrains. He knew he could fly through sparsely wooded areas; however, he would have to wend his way on foot in a dense forest. Upon arrival, he remained cautious. The woodlands were known to harbor other apex predators—wolves, cougars, and bears. Yet the forest was strangely quiet. The young dragon encountered no native predators or any other native species—not even birds. He assumed that they left because of his arrival. Indeed, they had fled from the area, but not because of him.

Another deadly creature was also patrolling the woodlands, looking for a meal. A lupucercopith (*lu*-pu-*cer*-kō-pĭth) had broken loose from its chains and escaped from its tormentors. It was a genetically-engineered hybrid with the baseline genome of a gray mountain wolf (*lupu-*) augmented with the genes of a baboon (*-cercopith*) (illustration 6). It had the basic body and coat of the former with the long snout, fangs, and temperament of the latter. Its development had been supplemented by somatostatin, a growth hormone. Hence, the hybrid was twice the size of a native wolf. None of its keepers were willing to engage the deadly creature.

The lupucercopith had been fed only scraps a few times a week to keep it hungry. Consequently, it was ravenous and would not hesitate to feed on anything within its reach.

Illustration 6: Lupucercopith

As a captive hybrid, the lupucercopith was not a creature of stealth. In its attempts to catch a meal, it had already run off all prey species in the area. Its only kill was a young faun that was too scrawny to abate the creature's hunger. So, the appearance of a much larger species was most enticing.

When the young dragon and the lupucercopith came face-to-face, the latter charged without hesitation. The youngster was not prepared for the savage onslaught of the hybrid. He was caught by surprise, accustomed to prey fleeing—not attacking. The hybrid had never encountered a dragon and was not daunted by the youngster's larger size.

In its initial attack, the hybrid's claws caught in the dragon's scales—essentially holding on to its prey. The young dragon reared back, narrowly avoiding the hybrid's reach for his throat. He fought ferociously, biting with his serrated teeth and beating the hybrid with his tail. The youngster's short spurts of fire only briefly hampered his adversary.

Just as the young dragon had no prior experience with hybrids, the lupucercopith had no prior experience with dragons. The youngster's attempt to become airborne was impeded by the trees and the weight of the hybrid hanging onto him. Still, his wing beats slapped the hybrid, further distracting it. In an attempt to dislodge his attacker, the youngster clamored up into the branches of a nearby tree. Still, the hybrid did not disengage. This proved to be a poor decision on the part of the hybrid. Clinging to the branches, the young dragon was able to reach down and seize the hybrid in his powerful jaws, ending its life. The young dragon suffered minor injuries thanks to his protective scales. He had learned a valuable, if impromptu, lesson in countering an attack and would remember it—along with the creature that ambushed him.

Intelligence

Like most mammals (including humans), dragons are quite intelligent and very perceptive. They can solve problems and use tools. They use their strong jaws and talons to pick up objects (e.g., rocks, branches) to build a structure (e.g., a barrier or a nest) or tear one down. They can join with other members and use their powerful wings to generate wind or create a barrier against it. Frigid gales often blow through the northeastern and arctic terrains, so the males will encircle a nesting site while the females tuck their eggs or chicks under their wings and up against their bodies for warmth. These decisions and actions are not instinctive. They are learned from parents, other clan members, and through experience.

Prudence

Dragons recognize the danger imposed by their fire. Just as a wild fire can destroy anything in its path, so can dragon fire. They teach their offspring to avoid using their fire unless they are under attack and have no other option for escape.

Dragons are well aware that the source of their fire is finite. Once that resource is depleted, a major weapon or tool is gone until their incendiary gland is replenished. Hence, dragons minimize the use of their fire unless there is a reason for it. For example, they will build a pyre of dead branches and brush among barren rocks and set it afire to cremate a fallen comrade or family member. They use their fire for offense and defense only when needed.

Atonement

There were two major events in which a dragon's decision resulted in a profound outcome for humans. A great gray dragon had agreed to support a treacherous man who was holding the dragon's injured mate hostage. The man told the dragon that a company of humans was going to attack him. If the dragon agreed to attack these humans first, the man would release the dragon's mate. Although the dragon was suspicious, he agreed. This decision led to the destruction of a human community, H'Aleth. The dragon unleased a firestorm, destroying their entire village (illustration 7).

The man who had made the bargain reneged and kept the dragon's disabled dragoness captive. Ironically, it was two survivors from the devastated village who freed her. Both the dragon and his dragoness never forgot their kindness. Years later, the dragon atoned for his earlier decision. When one of the former survivors cried out for help, he interceded in a battle that would have killed her and destroyed yet another community, Erwina. In a twist of fate, the same treacherous man that had once held his mate hostage was leading the battle. The two adversaries faced each other in a deadly duel (illustration 8).

Illustration 7: Firestorm

Memory

A dragon's memory lasts throughout its lifetime. Hence, over two to three centuries, a dragon accumulates a vast amount of experience and a wide array of knowledge, which it can apply throughout adulthood. Dragons hand down this knowledge to their offspring. They also share their knowledge with other clan members. Hence, they are aware of the habits and activities of other species, including humans. As with any species, a dragon's life and livelihood depend on acquired knowledge.

Language

Dragons utilize vocalizations to communicate. These vocalizations are similar to the low-frequency sounds that elephants generate. In the mountains, their rumblings reverberate off granite walls, echoing in canyons and throughout the aeries. These sounds can travel long distances and be heard by other dragons far away. It is one way they can stay in contact with each other even when they are separated by long distances. Since dragons possess echolocation, they can follow a sound to locate its source.

Most dragon vocalizations are below the threshold of human hearing. Sometimes, humans may hear a deep sound like distant rumbles of thunder. Dragons modulate the frequencies of their vocalizations depending on the meaning they wish to convey. Although they can learn to understand human language, they cannot articulate words as humans know them. Nevertheless, at a low frequency, they can simulate vocalizations in a manner that corresponds to syllables.

Once sound waves strike a human's eardrum, they are transmitted and interpreted by the auditory center of the brain as speech. Dragons have the ability to focus their sound projections to only the ear(s) of the individual(s) with whom they wish to communicate. This latter feature and the low frequency of their vocalizations have led to the misconception that dragons use telepathy.

Illustration 8: The Duel

Like other mammals, dragons are quite perceptive. They can interpret the intentions of other animals based on the latter's behavior and tone of voice. When interacting with humans, dragons can often discern human intentions to determine whether they are friend or foe.

Nonverbal Cues

During their migration, wherein subspecies of dragons settled into different niches, their dialects diverged. Although most of their communications remain intact, their tonal language varies. Nonverbal cues remain unchanged. These signals include dipping their heads in greeting or recognition, rocking their wings in acknowledgment, and banking to show or give direction. A sharp whip of the tail is a warning to back off or an indication of readiness to fight, whereas a tail curled around the body indicates nonaggression.

Supplemental Notes and Citations

In tonal language, a word can express different meanings based on the intonation (e.g., tone, pitch, emphasis) given to it or one of its syllables.

Vocalizations

Elephants have a complex system of vocalizations, including high-frequency sounds and low-frequency pulsated sounds for both long- and short-distance communication (Nair and Balakrishnan, 2009; Stoeger, *et al.*, 2021). They use trumpets, roars, rumbles, and even chirps for a variety of situations that include social interactions (e.g., contacting members within a herd and across other herds, during disturbances, and in dealing with aggressive behaviors).

CHAPTER 7
The Passing of a Patriarch

A Rare Event

At roughly 275 to 300 years of age—dragons did not keep count—a male red dragon died. He had been the patriarch of his clan, successfully guiding it into a stable, resourceful, and prudent family group. He had mentored most of its members before passing his alpha status on to another male who would continue to guide and protect the clan.

Although the old patriarch continued to mentor young dragons, after a while, his physical strength waned. He found he could not keep up with the adolescents. Other adult dragons took up that charge.

Over a period of only a few months, his strength faded rapidly. His clan recognized that the old dragon was dying and stayed close by as he slipped away.

High in the southwest mountains, a bright light flared suddenly, persisting for several minutes before disappearing as quickly as it had arisen. It was like an enormous bonfire that could be seen for miles—even in broad daylight. Yet it never spread beyond its origin.

These events were rare. Humans had observed and recorded the phenomena long before *Stella Ignis*. They continued to observe them after humans repopulated their territories after *Stella Ignis*.

The source of these sudden, short-lived flares was unknown. Unbeknownst to humans, these events occurred in the aeries of the red dragons. The bursts of bright light were the funeral pyres of deceased red dragons.

Life Span

Dragons are long-lived. They have one of the longest life spans of any mammal. In the absence of conflict, an adult dragon can live from 250 to 325 years. Their genetic ability to repair their own DNA is the primary reason for their longevity. Environmental factors and clashes with other species—or their own—can lead to an early death.

With their robust immune system, death from infection is rare among older chicks and adults. Yet disease is still the most common cause of an early death in newborn chicks. Nesting materials can carry a wide range of infectious agents. Hence, it is essential that chicks reach their mother's abdomen to lick the colostrum produced by her mammary glands. In addition to nutrients, colostrum contains vital maternal antibodies that provide immunity and prevent infections.

Environmental factors have a significant influence on a dragon's life span. Wide swings in temperature affect their habitats. For desert dwellers, including red dragons, extreme heat and lack of rain result in drought and loss of prey species. Fortunately, large aquifers underlie the grasslands and provide some relief for wildlife. Once the monsoon rains arrive, flooding replenishes the aquifers. The rains also turn rivers into torrents, which can sweep away and drown unwary, weak, or very immature animals—including unfledged dragon chicks.

For montane and subterranean dragons, earthquakes are disastrous. Their aeries may be destroyed, and some dragons may be trapped or crushed by falling debris. Prolonged exposure to subzero temperatures and blizzards—especially in the northern mountains—is a common cause of death in fledglings. If caught while away from their aery, they may not have the strength to battle the winds and may not be able to find their way home. Even an adult searching for the fledgling may not be able to find it.

In any environment, prolonged extremes of weather can adversely affect the very young and the very old. Immature and waning physiology may be unable to adapt in a timely manner—especially if shelter, food, and freshwater resources are constrained.

The life span of an unfledged chick varies. If they are lost, they are subject to predation by wolves, cougars, and other apex predators, including bounty hunters. Fledglings are less susceptible since they can become airborne. Even so, their reactions may not be quick enough to preclude a successful attack by an experienced predator. Hence, older adolescents and adult dragons keep a close eye on young offspring.

Dueling with another dragon is the most common cause of a premature death in adult dragons. Most of these clashes are due to an attempt by a male dragon—often a rogue—to take over a clan or part of its territory or to abscond with a female member of a clan. Although these battles usually result in the defeat and retreat of the loser, these fights can result in the death of a combatant.

Interactions with humans rarely result in the death of a dragon, due in large part to the efforts of both species to avoid each other. Hunters are the most common cause of human-induced injuries to dragons. Although arrows and spears can wound them, cannons and catapults can kill a dragon. Nonetheless, humans in some communities have protected dragon species and even aided them.

Supplemental Notes and Citations

Longevity

There are a number of animal species with long life spans (Edwards, *et al.*, 2019; Keane, *et al.*, 2015; Montero-Serra, *et al.*, 2018; Quesada, *et al.*, 2019). The bowhead whale (class *Mammalia*) has a life span of 200 years or more. It is the longest living mammal known to date. The Galapagos turtle (class *Reptilia*) has a similar life span. The Greenland shark (class *Chondrichthyes*) lives at least 250 years and may live up to 500 years. Mediterranean red coral (class *Anthozoa*) lives for 500 years. Humans (class *Mammalia*) have an estimated life span of 120 years.

Genetic and epigenetic factors play a significant role in determining longevity (Calnan and Brunet, 2008; Mayne, *et al.*, 2019; Vaiserman, *et al.*, 2017). Genetic factors affecting life span can be inherited. A family of FOX0 transcription factors can alter gene expression in response to environmental conditions (epigenetic factors). Thus, transitioning into a new environment—e.g., from grassy plains to frigid mountain ranges—

may be moderated by gene functions. Although life expectancy can change with changes in the environment, the outermost limit of life span does not change for a given species (Bozek, *et al.*, 2017). Currently, that limit appears to be 120 years in humans.

Colostrum

Colostrum is the first substance a newborn offspring receives upon nursing after birth. Mammalian colostrum, including human colostrum, contains critically important constituents, including immunoglobulins, vitamins, proteins, carbohydrates, and growth factors (Hammon, *et al.*, 2020; Kessler, *et al.*, 2020; Kim and Kim, 2020). Immunoglobulins provide protection against infectious agents while nutrition components influence the continued development and maturation of neonatal organ systems, including the immune system.

Part III
Hearth and Home

CHAPTER 8

Territories

Proper Introductions

A pair of great gray dragons—two brothers—flew into territory claimed by a clan of great gray dragons. The latter had inhabited the area for several generations. As was customary, sentinels kept watch over their territory and its boundaries. When a sentinel noted the two brothers' incursion, he watched them closely. The brothers had descended to a relatively low altitude, an indication that they were surveying the area. This raised the possibility that the two were hunting beyond their own territory—or were entertaining a possible takeover.

A dragoness in a nearby aery also spotted the duo. The two unknown males were not of her clan. As she watched, they flew overhead at a low altitude as if they were looking for something—or someone.

The dragoness promptly gathered up her two chicks and tucked them deep inside her cave. The dragons' surveillance made her suspicious that they were rogues who might attempt to overpower her or even kill her. If successful, they would kill her chicks. With her chicks safely hidden, she stood guard just inside the cave's entrance, where shadows hid her presence.

Soft, low-pitched rumbles from the dragoness echoed throughout the aery, which housed other members of her clan. Now they, too, were alerted to the two unknown dragons that had penetrated their territory. Theovolan, the alpha, was already aware and had lifted off to greet them.

Theovolan was the first and largest of three chicks raised long ago by his parents. His sire had been the alpha when he courted a dragoness from another nearby clan. When she accepted him, she joined his clan.

Flanked by two members of his clan, Theovolan approached the oncoming brothers. As they approached, the two brothers rocked their wings in greeting. In fact, they were not rogues. They were looking for mates who would be willing to join them and bolster their small clan.

Once proper introductions were made, Theovolan knew their clan's alpha, a distant cousin. The two brothers were welcome to stay for a visit, whereupon additional introductions might be in order.

Distinct Territories

All dragons are reclusive. The majority inhabit remote locations where predatory species, primarily humans, rarely venture. The great gray dragons live high along the south face of the northern mountain ranges, a terrain that is virtually inaccessible. These dragons only descend into the forested areas below except to hunt. Similarly, red dragons inhabit the southwestern mountains and patrol their high forests. Arctic dragons dwell on the north face of the northern mountains in the arctic and subarctic regions. Consequently, mountain-dwelling dragons must descend into the foothills, forests, and plains to hunt. Arboreal dragons make their homes in the giant trees of an ancient forest, where the weather and soil support the growth of sequoia and Douglas fir trees.

Red dragons and great gray dragons rarely interact. The vast distance between their two habitats has led to their social isolation. Although either species can easily fly to the other's territory, their respective habitats further discourage intermingling. The south is too hot for the great gray dragons, and the north is too cold for the red dragons. Grassland and woodlands lie between their two habitats.

Great gray dragons and arctic dragons do interact, albeit infrequently. Although a high mountain range lies between them, their respective mountain habitats are somewhat comparable. The range's northern face is cooler than the slightly warmer southern face. Below each mountain face, however, conditions are starkly different. To the north lies arctic tundra and ice. To the south, there are sunny hills and woodlands. Since the two territories do not overlap, there is no competition for food or nesting sites.

Freshwater river dragons' territories are shaped by water temperature, violently turbulent confluences, and physical barriers. Large boulders could force the dragons to rise out of the water and be seen by prey while narrow channels would block their passage.

Lake dragons inhabit land-locked bodies of water. Their territories can range from large lakes to inland seas, which may be found on the surface or underground in caverns. They also claim lands that surround their lakes. Since many lakes are found in mountainous regions, the territories of montane and lake dragons may overlap. Even so, there is very little competition since montane dragons tend to hunt in the foothills.

Marine dragons have no boundaries and tend to occupy waters favorable to them. They can cover long distances, often following prevailing currents or migrating prey species.

Distant Cousins

One day, a young dragon from a distant clan decided to survey remote territories. He was looking for a suitable nesting site before introducing himself to a prospective mate. Once he secured a site, he could begin courting females. The hunt for a home also gave him an opportunity to stretch his wings and possibly stumble onto something interesting. He did.

While aloft, the young dragon spotted an unescorted adolescent groping its way through some rocky foothills. On closer inspection, he saw that the adolescent was a young dragoness who was nudging one stone after another out of her way. A visual scan of the area revealed that the dragoness was unescorted. This was a hopeful sign, and he was intrigued.

The young dragon landed a respectful distance away. Facing her, he bowed his head in greeting, demonstrating that he was not aggressive. Then, he announced his name and identified the alpha of his clan.

Initially startled, the young dragoness perked up. She recognized his clan. A cousin had accepted a mate from that clan and ultimately joined it. So, she invited the young dragon to join her search for nesting stones. If he remained well-behaved, she would introduce him to her family.

Clans

Contrary to popular belief, dragons are social animals who live in tight-knit extended family groups. Usually, a specific male and female pair (the alphas) lead the clan. Unrelated members may be accepted into the clan. Typically, new clan members are usually mates of a female member since females often stay with their clan.

Dragons live in a cooperative, communal arrangement that all members of the clan support. Everyone, including juveniles, participate in caring for both the young and the old, as well as hunting and foraging for food. Older adolescents and adults defend their territory and protect other clan members. Clans will often succor an orphaned chick or unclaimed egg, even if it is not from one of their members.

To protect their respective territories, sentinels patrol from aloft. With their exquisite visual acuity and wide visual field, they can readily detect any potential threat. Large cave systems are highly prized and strongly defended. Many families can live in these locations. A clan may share part of its territory with offspring that wish to strike out on their own. This expands the number of eyes, ears, and noses keeping watch over the clan's territory.

Occasionally, a clan may accept a lone dragon or dragoness seeking to join it. Most often, these are individuals that have wearied of being on their own. When attempting to join a clan, the lone dragon or dragoness must defer and submit to the alpha dragon. Supplicants show submission by sitting upright, curling their tail around their body, and lowering their head. This puts the supplicant in a vulnerable position, indicating that he or she is not aggressive. Adapting this pose, however, can also be a subterfuge on the part of a rogue intending to infiltrate the clan and take control of it. Although this rarely occurs, clan members keep a sharp eye on a newcomer's behavior until he or she is thoroughly integrated.

Over time, a clan can become too large, triggering a need to divide. Insufficient resources and overcrowding can prompt a split. Usually, a mature adult will relocate his extended family to another setting within reach of his original aery. Such separations are congenial, and members of both clans remain allied.

When clan members are closely related, their territories may overlap. Security is bolstered substantially when multiple related clans have overlapping territories. Help is never far away.

Usurpers

Occasionally, a rogue or lone dragon will attempt to usurp control of a clan if he thinks he can overpower the alpha. A challenger who wants to be the dominant male keeps his head held high and his tail positioned to strike a blow. If the clan's extended family includes several adult males, a lone male dragon will not set a challenge.

If the clan is young with only one mature male, a challenge is more likely—with the two males squaring off. This does not ensure that the challenger will be victorious. Although smaller, a dragoness has the same armaments and will join her mate in fending off the challenger. If chicks are threatened, both parents and any mature siblings will engage the usurper as well.

Should the challenger dragon succeed in killing the lone male, the dragoness will still defend her offspring. Should he overcome her, the rogue will kill the offspring and cannibalize any eggs. Thus, these battles are bloody.

When dragons are engaged in mortal combat, dragon fire is not used in close contact. Both contestants would immolate each other along with anything else in the area that will burn.

Supplemental Notes and Citations

Territoriality

Species declare and delineate their territory by a mix of vocalizations, scent marking, scratching, behavioral displays, and attacks to defend it (Giuggioli, *et al.*, 2011; Potts & Lewis, 2014). Some territories may overlap as long as the populations inhabiting them manage to avoid each other—possibly via physical evidence indicating how recently the other occupants have passed through the area. Conversely, some species may share the same territory so long as they are not competing for the same resources—and are not predator and prey. For example, zebras and giraffes share the same territory. Zebras graze on grass whereas giraffes graze on tree leaves (Schmidt, *et al.*, 2016).

CHAPTER 9
Hunting

A Thwarted Ambush

In a mountain aery, two very active great gray dragon chicks were getting stronger and bigger and were beginning to test their wings. They had fully transitioned to eating meat only, still turning up their noses at fruit and nuts. At twelve weeks, the chicks were large enough and their scales strong enough for them to leave the nest under parental supervision. It would be a while before they could fly. Nevertheless, it was time for them to begin learning how to hunt.

So, they tagged along with their mother on hunting forays. As these expeditions were the chicks' first hunting lessons, they were confined to the ground since they were not yet fledged. If danger arose, the chicks could still duck under their mother's wings for protection.

Normally, dragons are primarily aerial predators. With unfledged chicks, the dragoness stalked her prey on the ground. As her chicks remained vulnerable to predators, she had to stay vigilant for both prey and predators. After finding a nook among some granite boulders, she stashed her two chicks there and settled below them. Then she folded her wings tightly against her body, wove her tail and neck around rocks and debris, and finally nestled her head among some stones. Having blended into the terrain, she lay perfectly still and waited for unsuspecting prey to come within her considerable reach.

A short time later, a stocky animal sauntered into view along the edge of the woodlands below. It had grayish-brown fur, a black-and-white stripe across its narrow face, a short tail, and impressive front claws. The dragoness dismissed the badger as too small to be an adequate meal, so she made no move to acquire it. This was all good and well until the male chick decided to tackle it.

The young dragon began weaving his way toward his intended prey while his sister laid low and stayed still. Meanwhile, a cougar on higher ground had spotted the badger and was stalking it when the chick began its ambush. The chick was much closer and an easier catch than the badger. So, the cougar switched targets.

When the dragoness spotted her chick stalking a badger and a cougar stalking her chick, she immediately broke cover. The moment she arose, both the cougar and the badger bolted. Her ambush thwarted, the dragoness collected her two startled offspring and headed back to their aery.

Hunting

All dragons are apex predators. Their prey consists of mammals (preferably large), large birds (infrequently), large reptiles (occasionally), and fish (variable) depending on the species of dragon (illustration 9). Land-based dragons also eat fruits, nuts, seeds, and berries.

Typically, land-based dragons prefer to hunt by air. With raptor-like vision, dragons can spot prey from long distances; however, they are not above using subterfuge. When hunting in a rocky terrain, dragons can camouflage themselves on escarpments, ledges, and near huge boulders—like an ambush predator. Hunting in woodland terrain is another matter altogether. Dragon feet are neither dainty nor padded or tufted. In a lightly wooded terrain, a young juvenile could tread lightly and achieve some measure of stealth. An adult dragoness can achieve stealth if the canopy is dense, the ambient light is low, and there is little litter on the ground. Although adult male dragons can affect some measure of stealth under the right conditions, they typically disregard any notion of being undetected in a forested area. They simply stomp their way through the trees and vegetation. As a result, the males rarely catch prey in a wooded area unless they can flush it out into the open.

As a general rule, both male and female dragons hunt; however, adult males patrol the clan's territory. Female dragons are smaller, slenderer, and can blend into wooded terrains and rocky formations. Great gray dragons can curl both tail and neck around their body along a rock formation so they look like a boulder. They can thread their way through loosely forested foothills and blend into deep shade provided by rocky overhangs.

Illustration 9: The Hunt

Arctic dragons do not swim *per se*. They fold their wings tightly against their bodies, close their nostrils, execute a plunge dive that is relatively shallow, and begin to curve upward almost immediately upon entry. Thus, arctic dragons must execute a precision dive to capture prey. Their precision is due, in part, to their ability to detect an electric field and determine the direction their prey is headed. The speed of the dive provides enough momentum to allow the dragon to resurface and resume flight. The wing compression is so tight that the scales overlap and protect the underlying lanugo from getting wet.

Freshwater river and lake dragons have similar capabilities; however, they prefer to hunt prey near the water's edge or in the water. River dragons use rapidly flowing water for camouflage. Lake dragons submerge until only their snout and eyes appear above water level, then strike when their target comes within range. To catch prey on land, they must leave the water to become airborne.

A Mouthful of Feathers

An adolescent river dragon had just finished surfing the category II rapids of a briskly flowing tributary to the River Della. The tributary coursed through both open and forested terrain. The dragon's trip downstream was easy. He simply had to go with the flow while avoiding any impediments. The trip back upstream was another matter altogether. He could either swim against a strong current or take to the air and fly back home. The young dragon decided to test his mettle against the current.

Some distance upstream, the dragon espied a sand bar along the river that bordered on some woodlands—a perfect place for a brief respite. Shortly after sprawling out on the sand bar, he heard a splash and the wing beat of a bird. An eagle had snatched a fish from the stream and landed further up on the sand bar. In focusing on his catch, the eagle ignored the grayish-blue clump of woody debris farther away downstream. The debris soon found its way into the river and disappeared. Moments later, the dragon launched toward the eagle. Reacting instantly, the eagle took off, leaving the dragon with a mouthful of feathers and a half-eaten trout.

At least his effort had brought him further upstream.

Marine and Brackish Water Dragons

Marine dragons cannot fly. Their fins are modified wings adapted to propel them though water instead of air. Their long tail serves as both rudder and whip. Using both fins and tail, they can reach speeds of nearly fifty miles per hour (approximately forty-three knots) underwater. Although they have lost the ability of sustained flight, they can use their modified wings and a whip of their tail to launch out of the water, either in a breach or to seize low-flying prey.

Brackish-water dragons hunt on land and in water. Similar to arctic dragons, they have adapted to hunt underwater while still maintaining the ability to take flight.

Let Predators Beware

As a general rule, dragons avoid contact with humans, who are their only known predator. Yet dragons have recognized instances in which humans have intervened to protect a vulnerable dragon, dragon chick, or egg. Some clans of red and great gray dragons maintain a tacit understanding with some communities of people and have an accord not to hunt each other.

To preclude any confusion about prey species, *H. transformans* scouts who venture near or into dragon territories do so as humans until the dragons can recognize them in their alternate species. Native wild animals—all potential prey species—bolt at the site of a dragon. *Homo transformans* scouts in their alternate species, however, simply wait and watch for the dragon to approach.

The arrangement above does not include bounty hunters. Emboldened by the prospect of riches, bounty hunters kill dragons for their decorative scales, their horns, and their eggs. They target any wayward juvenile should there be no watchful parent nearby.

Whereas arrows cannot bring down an adult dragon of any species, archers can kill a chick or a young juvenile whose scales are not fully developed. Hunters can kill an adult dragon under two conditions: 1) they have weapons that can penetrate a dragon's thick scales, and 2) they can fire from outside the range of a dragon's fire. Red dragons, who are much smaller than the great grays, can be killed by a large spear launched from a catapult. Great gray dragons can be killed by carefully aimed cannon fire.

The notion of raiding an aery and capturing a dragon—even a baby dragon—is out of the question. Clan members will join forces to defend their aeries and protect their offspring. They have the advantage of occupying high ground, whereas hunters must climb to reach an aery. Dragons also have the advantage of camouflage. A great gray dragon's drab gray coloring blends into the northern mountains, providing the perfect conditions to affect an ambush of their own. Similarly, a red dragon's variegated coloring blends into the southwest mountains. Finally, all species of dragons use their astounding flight capability to defend their young by raining fire down upon any attacker from almost any direction.

CHAPTER 10
Reproduction

The Rebuke

In the sparsely wooded foothills of the northeastern mountains, an adult great gray dragoness and her adolescent daughter were hunting game. The adult was teaching her offspring to stalk prey on the ground. Unbeknownst to either of them, a male great gray dragon had spotted them. A lone male—a rogue that held no territory—immediately targeted the adult dragoness. If he could overpower her, he could mate with her.

Adult male great gray dragons are massive. Although they can blend against a mountain or a large rock formation, they can't hide their massive bulk among trees. They knocked them down. When taking off or landing, adult males require open space. Once on the ground, they can wend their way through a lightly wooded terrain. Thus, from his place among the crags above the foothills, the rogue found his way around the rocks as he descended into the foothills.

As the dragon crept into the sparsely wooded area, a brisk mountain breeze rustled through the leaves and the leaf litter below, covering the sound of his approach. Focused on her efforts to track prey, neither the dragoness nor her offspring detected the dragon's advance until the clouds shifted, allowing a little more sunlight to filter through the trees. It was enough to cast the dragon's tall shadow over the dragoness. She recognized the shape instantly and knew at once it was not her mate. Turning toward the dragon, she issued a deep rumble that resounded across the foothills and into the mountains. It was a warning to keep away—a rebuke. The rogue disregarded it.

The aggressive male initially accosted the youngster. He had no interest in her other than getting her out of his way. With a whip of his tail, he knocked her aside. Furious, the dragoness positioned herself between her offspring and the male. This attack would not go unanswered. She issued another even more forceful rumble as she faced off with her aggressor. The young dragoness, back on her feet, took up her mother's call, repeating it as forcefully as she could.

When the dragon tried to force himself on the dragoness, he was met with razor-sharp teeth and equally sharp talons. As they fought, the battle took them beyond the woodlands. This was the dragoness's intent. By retreating, she had drawn her attacker away from her daughter and into open terrain. Any kinsmen who heard her calls could see them. She dared not break free of him to take flight lest he turn on her offspring.

Suddenly, the rogue abruptly turned and abandoned the object of his desire. Another dragon, the clan's alpha, was diving toward him at a high speed, followed by two more males—members of the dragoness's clan who were responding to her calls. In the heat of the moment, an amorous dragon could forget that rumbles echo through the mountains and can be heard for miles.

As the rogue turned to retreat, the alpha slammed into him. The other two dragons flanked the dragoness and her youngster for their protection. Meanwhile, the two antagonists engaged in a violent but brief battle (illustration 10). They were not evenly matched. The alpha was substantially larger and more experienced. He soundly defeated the rogue, who quickly retreated and was allowed to fly away.

Family Matters: Courtship and Reproduction

It is not uncommon for a lone dragon to encounter and attempt to approach an unescorted dragoness. This can be quite a testy situation. A dragoness will rebuff an unknown male, especially if she already has a mate. If the dragon withdraws or keeps his distance, there is no issue.

When courting a dragoness, an amorous suitor demonstrates his capabilities through aerial maneuvers. He exhibits his agility, stamina, power, and skill by maneuvering around canyons and outcroppings and diving into and out of canyons at high speed. To prove his hunting prowess, he might provide a large and powerful animal such as a bear, boar, or bison for dinner.

Illustration 10: The Rebuke

If the amorous dragon is a red dragon, he may show off his most handsome features. The features that are most attractive and alluring include long, intricately curved horns and bright, striking scales that reflect many fanciful colors—especially in flight.

When a female accepts a male's attentions, both will curl their tails around the other's body, intertwine their necks, and caress each other with their muzzles.

Reproduction

After a suitable courtship, the male will mount the dragoness and fertilize her eggs. Most land-based dragons mate for life. Marine dragons tend to be solitary with the female raising the offspring of a mating.

Breeding is not limited to the alpha pair. Any member of the clan can mate and produce offspring as long as the two are not closely related. Inbreeding is avoided. Interbreeding with other clans often establishes or strengthens relationships with another clan and promotes genetic diversity.

Like other monotremes, dragons lay eggs; however, the shells of dragon eggs are not hard like those of birds. They are soft and leathery, consistent with those of other monotreme species. Although eggs are fertilized inside the dragoness's body, they are incubated outside by both parents. For land-based dragons, the size of a typical clutch is two to three eggs.

Marine dragonesses are ovoviviparous. They produce a single egg and incubate it internally until it hatches, after which the dragoness gives birth underwater. Given the large size of the egg, which must accommodate a marine chick, there is only enough room for one egg. If the dragoness produces two eggs, she may become "egg-bound" and unable to give birth—a life-threatening condition.

When sufficiently mature, a marine chick breaks out of its leathery shell, which triggers contractions in the mother, leading to the birth of the chick. The dragoness promptly gathers the chick with her fins and directs it to her abdomen to begin feeding. Unlike land-based chicks, the offspring have vestigial forelimbs with "milk" talons that it uses to cling to its mother. Eventually, the chick's forelimbs and talons drop off as their flippers develop so the youngster can keep up with its mother.

Nesting Behaviors

Mountain dragons build their nests among the higher crags—often in caves with narrow entrances, where predators cannot get past a parent. They prefer a deeply recessed nesting site, preferably in tectonic caves or caverns. Multiple family nests can occupy a large tectonic cave system that is recessed deep in the mountainside. The twists and turns along passageways formed by fracture lines shelter these sites from cold winter winds.

When a dragoness identifies a suitable nesting site, both partners gather materials to build a nest. Unlike most mammals, they do not use vegetation of any type in the nest. They use stones, the majority of which are obtained from rapidly flowing mountain streams. These stones are rounded and smooth with no sharp edges. Large stones with at least one smooth side form the border. Inside, small, rounded stones are interspersed in a large amount of dirt for the interior of the nest to cushion the eggs. The dragoness pulls off some of her lanugo undercoat to provide soft bedding for the soft-shelled, leathery eggs.

Nesting caves are kept warm by brief bursts of dragon fire, heating the walls of a cave or tunnels (if any) radiating through the cave or cavern system. The dragoness curls her tail and neck around the nest and covers it with her head. Oftentimes, if the male is present, he will lie with his back to the cave's entrance to block cold air in the winter.

Like eagles, arboreal dragons build their nests deep within the canopy of tall Douglas firs and sequoia trees, nearly 300 feet above the ground. Nests must be high enough to deter almost any predator yet not so high to be threatened by storms or gale force winds. Hence, they avoid building nests in treetops.

Parents build their nest in a cluster of trees with a dense canopy and overlapping, intertwined branches that can support the weight of both parents, the nest, and the chicks. Nests are constructed from materials derived from trees distant from the nest site. Tactically, this hides the location of the nest and camouflages it. The combination of height, foliage, and large tree limbs keeps nests from being seen from the ground.

Both river and lake dragons dig a deep underwater channel to a location above the waterline where they excavate their nests. The waterline must be far enough underground to support the den and prevent any den scent from reaching the surface. Subterranean dragons locate a suitable site deep underground, often a niche within a cavern system.

Nesting materials for freshwater aquatic and arboreal dragon species consist of a variety of branches, leaves, moss, and other vegetation gathered from the surrounding terrain. Occasionally, fur and feathers from prey species and lanugo shed by a parent may cushion the inside of the nest.

The *Odontis Pristis*, a semiaquatic swamp dragon, creates a nest in sandy terrain. The dragoness lays two to three eggs in the sand, covers them up, and guards them until they hatch. The offspring are ambulatory and able to swim from birth. In the absence of immediate danger, the mother and chicks will stay on land until the chicks are old enough to eat meat.

Supplemental Notes and Citations

Genetic Diversity

When two unrelated members of the same species mate, the mix of genes leads to diversity in offspring. Inbreeding leads to decreased genetic diversity, which increases the risk that any abnormal genes could be paired and subsequently expressed in offspring.

Oviparous

Similar to birds and reptiles, all monotremes lay eggs and incubate them outside the mother's body (Renfree and Shaw, 2001). They are the only mammalian species to do so.

CHAPTER 11
Raising Offspring

A Wayward Chick

An exuberant young dragon, not yet fledged, spotted a small rodent scurrying among the rocks and boulders of his mother's aery. It was a mountain pica—a furry rodent about eight inches long. Intrigued, the youngster watched it for a moment, tracking its movements. Instinctively, he remained perfectly still, his gray scales blending into the rocks.

The youngster had long since been weaned from his mother's milk and was eating meat provided by his parents. The pica represented a small snack—if he could catch it. The inexperienced chick lunged for his anticipated treat and missed. The pica had other plans and darted into a small passageway among the rocks.

The chick gave chase. The pica avoided getting caught by darting into a narrow niche in the rocks. The opening was too small for the chick to follow. Undaunted, the chick scratched at the opening with his talons. He managed to dislodge a small rock, widening the opening just enough to reach inside it.

Not to be outdone, the pica dodged the chick's reach. It scampered across a razor-thin ridge into a crack on the rock face. The chick promptly pursued the rodent only to find himself dangling from the precipice—barely hanging on to the same crack harboring the pica. At this point, the rock face was essentially smooth. The razor-thin ridge offered no footing for the much larger chick.

The chick was in dire straits. He could not fly out of his dilemma. If he let go of the crack, he would fall to his death. The distressed chick cried out with a high-pitched rumble. His cry brought the dragoness to his—and the pica's—rescue. As his mother took her wayward chick back to the safety of the nest, the pica scampered back across the ridge and went on its way.

Raising Chicks

Dragon offspring have much to learn about the world around them. Survival is more than a matter of instinct. Parents, older siblings, and adult relatives watch over their young, guiding them into and out of a variety of situations. Lessons in avoiding humans and other predators are paramount. A youngster's greatest threat comes from bounty hunters and hybrid creatures.

Fortunately, chicks and fledglings are rarely lost to predation. Close adult supervision keeps them safe. Even so, an unwary and adventurous youngster could be lost to a hungry predator. Thus, predators remain a threat until offspring can make fire and target it accurately as older adolescents.

Lactation, Growth, and Development

Offspring learn to identify their parents both by smell and by the sound of their rumbles. When newborn dragons first hatch, they identify their mother from her scent. The dragoness has milk glands on her abdomen, which open onto the surface of the skin. As soon as the chicks break out of their shell and tumble into the nesting materials, they try to locate their mother. Drawn by the scent of milk, they attempt to climb out of the nest to reach her. Although land-based dragon chicks are ambulatory at birth, they are wobbly. Initially, the mother lifts each chick out of the nest and places it on her abdomen to feed. After a few days, the chicks are expected to transport themselves.

Squabbles

Two feisty chicks were clamoring to get out of their nest. They smelled their mother's milk and wanted to reach her to feed. Meanwhile, their mother was resting beside the nest, waiting for her chicks to find their way over the mound of rocks that formed their nest. At birth, their motor skills were sufficiently developed to stumble around inside the nest. The next step was to develop the strength and coordination required to leave the nest unaided.

The smooth edges of the nest allowed the chicks to scale the rocks without injury. Fortunately, the rocks were not aligned evenly, leaving gaps among them. Where present, these gaps offered footholds. As soon as one chick found a promising location, the other chick attempted to move in, climbing over his or her sibling. Then the two would start squabbling over who had the right of way. At that point, the dragoness intervened. Their scales were not sufficiently developed to protect them against the talons, teeth, and claws each one already possessed.

After a few days of climbing on their mother's abdomen, land-based dragon chicks become skillful enough to get onto their mother's back for transport. Marine dragon chicks can swim from birth and, with guidance from the mother, rise to the surface for air. The mother will turn on her side to let her chick nurse until it is ready to eat meat.

Growing Up

At one to two months of age, chicks are introduced to a meat diet; however, they continue to take their mother's milk for another two or three months. The immunoglobulins in the mother's milk protect her offspring until their immune system is mature. After three or four months, the chicks are weaned. By nine months, they are using their wings to keep up with their mother, which strengthens their wing muscles as well.

At twelve months, land-based youngsters can sustain flight, albeit at lower speeds, and glide for short distances. Once dragon offspring are mobile, both male and female members of the clan or pod take care of them. Older adolescents (two to three years old) tend to the nursery while both young adults (three to five years old) and mature adults hunt, guard, and defend the clan and its territory.

Parenting

As a rule, the dragoness tends to the nest, the eggs, and the chicks once hatched. Her mate provides food for her and the newly hatched chicks. Other family members can bring food as well. The sire tends to the nest when the dragoness leaves to get water, which also allows her to stretch her body before returning to nesting duties. At times, other female relatives also tend the nest to give both parents a break. Unrelated or rowdy visitors are rebuked until the chicks are nimble enough to get out of the way.

When a chick shows evidence of readiness to fly, both parents cruise by the nest slowly to encourage the chick to come to them. If the chick is unable to achieve or sustain flight, both parents are available to catch it. When finally fledged, either parent will accompany the chick on short flights. This serves two purposes: to give the chick opportunities to strengthen its wings and to orient the chick toward the location of its aery. As the chick becomes more robust, its flights lengthen and provide the chick with a broader view of its clan's territory.

Chicks do not go to ground until they are strong enough to lift off from a ledge or other outcropping effortlessly. Once this skill is well practiced, both parents will take the chick to ground. They protect their offspring as it begins to learn its way around ground level. If the situation becomes dangerous, one parent can lift off with the chick while the other provides cover.

Sparring Lessons

Fledglings and juveniles of both genders often play with each other. Young adult dragons will spar with each other to hone their skills and test their respective strengths. Even chicks engage in rough-and-tumble with each other under the watchful eye of an adult. Both male and female offspring test their skills side by side so their maneuvers will be coordinated in a joint assault to counter a threat.

Juveniles hone their skills through athletic activities. Aerial tests of agility and strength are quite common. Juveniles will fly through narrow canyons or crevices, race at high altitudes, and dive at high speeds in a game of chase. Testing aerial combat skills is hazardous. In a mock battle, bites and talons can cause serious wounds, and wings and talons can become tangled. If the combatants cannot disengage, both could crash into the ground from a very high altitude—a lethal event for both of them.

Hunting Lessons

Hunting lessons begin when a chick is fully mobile—even though the youngster is not yet old enough or strong enough to tackle prey.

Once a chick is able to traverse on land and lift off to become airborne, the youngster graduates from chick to fledgling and rapidly matures into a juvenile.

First, juveniles must learn which species are prey and which are not. Identification of predators comes first, with hybrid creatures at the top of the list. Then, juveniles learn to distinguish native species from humans who have transformed by recognizing the differences in the scent and behavior of a transformed human. Native species will bolt immediately when confronted with a threat, whereas transformed species tend to wait and watch. Hybrid creatures wait for no one and attack on sight. Next, youngsters must learn patience: when to remain still—an almost impossible task for a newly minted juvenile—and how to use stealth when stalking prey. Finally, they must learn how to hunt both on the ground and from aloft.

Initially, both parents use the capture-and-release method to train their youngsters to hunt animals on the ground. Adult dragons do not feed on the offspring of other species. They target larger prey animals, often the male of the species, for the amount of food a larger animal provides. So, when parents bring back live prey, a juvenile is allowed to play with it. At this point, no harm is intended. The parents want their offspring to learn the scent, sounds, and appearance of the species. Subsequently, the "prey" is released and returned to its own species.

Parents also teach their offspring how to hunt prey while in flight, further developing the juvenile's hunting skills. Catching prey on the fly comes naturally. Red and arboreal dragons easily master the skills required for landing on and taking off from the ground efficiently. It is another matter altogether for a great gray dragon. Juveniles can land and take off with no problem. Adult males, however, must lumber across the landscape or launch from a cliff or an escarpment to get off the ground.

Eventually, the juveniles are large enough and strong enough to hunt adult animals. Initially, they go on supervised hunts to sharpen their skills. Lessons continue through adolescence until offspring demonstrate the skills to hunt independently.

Part IV
There Be Dragons

CHAPTER 12
Montane Dragons

A Restless Planet

When the tension and friction between two unyielding tectonic plates built up to a critical level, one plate gave way. The upper plate rose, allowing the lower plate to slip beneath it. The tectonic shift released an enormous amount of stored energy, causing a massive earthquake.

When a tremor shuddered through the aeries of a great gray dragon clan, the adults reacted immediately. A fissure had opened. It became progressively longer and deeper, shaking boulders loose and breaking off ledges. Tons of rock were falling from the face of the mountain, threatening the stability of their nests.

Conditions deteriorated rapidly, forcing parents and older siblings to carry unfledged chicks and eggs to safety. Yet even a mature dragon can carry only two offspring or eggs at a time—one in each talon. Furthermore, finding a safe location was relative. It might be far away and offer little shelter. Sometimes a neighboring clan would harbor the refugees unless the tremors threatened them as well.

Parents and their adolescents risked their lives with every trip they made back to their aeries. In the meantime, other adults were also in danger. The earthquake had opened a new chasm which threatened their nests. In an attempt to stabilize the fissure and protect their nests, the adults used their fire to weld the rocks and boulders that had fallen into the chasm. Yet not even a great gray dragon can withstand the crushing blow of mountain granite. Many lives were lost that day, as fatally injured adults and nests with unfledged chicks and eggs fell into the abyss.

All montane species are closely related genetically (genotype) while developing physical characteristics (phenotype) that support adaptation to their respective environments.

Great Gray Dragons (Dragonis Fuscus Magna)
A Robust Physique

Great gray dragons are the largest and most powerful of the three most common species of land-based dragons (illustration 11). They live in the northern and northeastern mountains, where their aeries reach up to 14,000 feet. They are well acclimated to these altitudes and are rarely seen in the foothills. Nevertheless, they hunt in montane forests and investigate violent or tumultuous incidents in territories below the mountains.

Illustration 11: Gray Dragon

Shades of gray to charcoal color with no markings give great grays a drab appearance despite their handsome features. The darker color allows for greater absorption of sunlight in cooler climates. This blends in well with their habitat and allows these dragons to meld into mountainside, as if they were a part of it. They can remain very still for prolonged periods, thereby becoming essentially invisible to the human eye. The dorsal surfaces of a great gray dragon's body are covered with thick keratin plates. Their ventral surfaces are covered by plates that are lighter in both thickness and color.

Great gray dragons are massive. Their body size ranges from twenty to twenty-six feet, not including the neck and the tail. The head and neck add six to eight feet, and the tail adds eighteen to twenty-four feet in length. Their wingspan is forty to forty-six feet. Their soaring speed is 180–240 mile per hour, and their diving is 250 miles per hour. Given their size, great gray dragons can barely lumber at fifteen miles per hour on the ground. Their fire reaches thirty-five to forty-five feet, and they have a bite force of 1,200 pounds per square inch. Given their robust wingspan, flight altitudes can easily reach 18,000 feet.

Living On the Edge

Great gray dragons established their aeries high in the northern mountain range. The range extended from east to west and was still actively expanding. Built by tectonic activity, with one tectonic plate sliding under another, the mountains were forced ever upward, causing fractures in the land below. Earthquakes created slip faults which, in turn, caused the land to subside. Although there was no volcanic activity, tremors often disturbed the aeries of the great gray dragons. The mountain's instability threatened the caves and caverns that many montane dragons used to house their nests and shelter their chicks.

Still, the mountains offered a secure refuge from hunters. A few prey species had adapted to life high in the northern mountains—leopards, antelope, sheep, bears, foxes. These animals were also reclusive. So, montane dragons frequently descended into the montane forests to hunt.

Red Dragons (Dragonis Rubra)
A Lithe Physique

Red dragons are so named for their reflective scales (illustration 12). They inhabit the southern and southwestern mountains, and their aeries range from 9,000 to 11,000 feet. A relatively slender animal by dragon standards, they are the smallest of the montane dragon species. More lithe and agile than their larger cousins, their bodies offer more flexibility and nimbleness. Their sylphlike, aerodynamic shape enables them to attain greater flight and diving speeds than other montane dragons. Given their relatively slender frame, they can also achieve running speeds of thirty to thirty-five miles per hour.

Illustration 12: Red Dragon

Red dragons are stunningly beautiful—both on the ground and in flight. Their thinner, lighter, and very colorful scales reflect sunlight and shimmer. Amber to reddish-brown is their baseline color, with iridescent streaks of blue and green intermixed. Additional streaks of gold flow from the top of the head down to the neck. Different combinations of mineral salts are the source of these colors. In reflecting sunlight, their scales also help cool the dragons in summer.

Males are distinguished by their curved horns, which they begin to develop when they are ten to twelve years old. Females do not have horns. Red dragons stand twelve to seventeen feet tall at the shoulders with all four legs on the ground. Their body length is fourteen to twenty feet, not including the head, neck, and tail. The head and neck add six to eight feet (not including horns), and the tail adds another twelve to sixteen feet. Wingspans range from thirty-two to thirty-eight feet.

As the lightest and most slender of the montane dragons, they are the fastest and most agile. They are the falcons of the dragon species, with a soaring speed of 160–220 miles per hour and a diving speed of 250–300 miles per hour. They can also achieve a speed of thirty to thirty-five miles per hour on the ground. Their fire reaches twenty to twenty-five feet, and their bite force is 500 pounds per square inch.

Life Under the Meridian Sun

Red dragons range in the southern and southwestern mountains and forests, extending into the grasslands below. Much older than the northern range, the southwestern mountains had been etched by erosion, creating many hidden nooks and crannies. These places provided refuge for many species of animals, including the red dragons. Clusters of brush and hidden pools of water, protected from the sun, sustained the wildlife inhabiting these mountains. Both vegetation and pools were restored during violent summer thunderstorms.

The highest elevations provided ideal nesting sites for the red dragons. The majority of their prey species inhabited the foothills and grasslands below, where wildlife was plentiful. Rivers flowing from the north fed the grasslands, which were lush compared to the scrub vegetation found in the mountains. Spring rains and subterranean rivers restored a huge aquifer beneath the grasslands, spotting them with pools of water.

Humans are the only known predators of red dragons. Bounty hunters sought their colorful scales, curved horns, and eggs. They were nearly hunted to extinction before they came under the protection of sympathetic humans who had established small, scattered villages throughout the grasslands.

Arctic Dragons (Dragonis Arcturus Alba)
A Sleek Physique

Although smaller and slenderer than their gray counterparts, arctic dragons are much larger than the red dragons (illustration 13). Given that their mountains face the fury of arctic storms and avalanches, their aeries are located at lower altitudes. This facilitates a rapid evacuation in the event of an avalanche and prevents them from being entombed by ice and snow.

Arctic dragons have gray coloring on top of their head, back, and wings which absorb the sun's radiation. Their chest, underbelly, and underside of their wings are almost pure white. They are covered with relatively thin scales that compress tightly for diving.

These dragons are sixteen to eighteen feet tall at the shoulders, standing on all four legs. Body length ranges from eighteen to twenty-four feet (not including the head, neck, and tail). The head and neck add an additional eight to ten feet, and the tail adds sixteen to eighteen feet. With a wingspan of thirty to forty-two feet, their soaring speed is 150–180 miles per hour, and their diving speed is 230–260 miles per hour. They can achieve a speed of twenty to twenty-five miles per hour on the ground. Their fire reaches thirty to forty feet, and they have a bite force of 850 pounds per square inch.

A Land of Extremes

Arctic dragons inhabit arctic and subarctic regions beyond the northern mountains. They have no known predators. Unlike their montane cousins, arctic dragons are semiaquatic. Although they do not swim *per se*, they can fold their wings tightly against their bodies, close their nostrils, and execute a plunge dive to capture fish and other prey. The tight wing compression forces the scales to overlap and protect the underlying lanugo from becoming wet. Their dives are relatively shallow and begin to curve almost immediately upon entry. The speed of the dive provides enough momentum to allow the dragon to resurface and resume flight.

Arctic dragons must execute precision dives to capture prey. With the ability to detect a prey's electric field, they can target and track prey with accuracy.

Illustration 13: Arctic Dragoness

An Arctic Playground

High in a northern mountain range, an arctic dragoness led her two fledged chicks to an unusual freshwater lake. The lake's waters were comfortably warm, heated underneath by a deep, volcanic magma chamber. The lake sported a wide variety of fish and provided many arctic wildlife species with much needed warmth. The dragoness took her chicks to the edge of the lake where the water was shallow. It was a good place for her youngsters to learn how to execute a dive.

When the chicks reached the edge of the lake and saw all the fish, they immediately took to the water. Swimming came naturally to them. They chased one fish after another—to no avail. Yet, in doing so, they instinctively executed partial dives.

For the present, the fish had the advantage. Before the chicks could catch one, they would need to master echolocation and learn how to recognize the electric fields emitted by fish. In the meantime, the chicks were enjoying their personal arctic swimming pool.

CHAPTER 13

Freshwater Aquatic Dragons

Dragonenesis Dragonis Fluminibus
The River Della

A dragoness watched over her two youngsters as they frolicked in the upper River Della, a large river far north of its juncture with the River Lacus. Here, the waters were deep, crisp, and cold and flowed rapidly. Although humans occupied the region, they had only a few settlements in the north. Most were concentrated primarily in the east and the south. Except for wildlife, including river dragons, the territory was largely uninhabited.

Initially, even before they were fledged, the youngsters had become skillful swimmers in small streams near their den. They had achieved this milestone by chasing after an assortment of fish that did not want to be their next meal. One day, they would become skilled hunters of both fish and game.

Once the youngsters were fledged and could take flight directly from the ground, their mother took them to a shallow river where they could practice taking off from water. This was no easy task. Although their back feet had webbing, this alone did not provide sufficient lift in water. A youngster needed more power and speed to launch its body far enough out of the water to bring its wings into play. Youngsters gained this strength by swimming against the river's current.

After much practice, the youngsters finally graduated to the River Della. With a depth of 175–200 feet and a width of three to five miles, the river provided ample cover and space for both the dragoness and her juvenile offspring. It also sported category II and III rapids, where the youngsters could practice surfing and dodging rocks. This training would serve them well should they venture farther south one day, where the rapids were category IV and V.

These excursions were not without peril. The offspring had not yet developed the ability to make and control fire. So, their mother kept a sharp eye on the waters. Dragons were not the only species to traverse the River Della. Although most of the other denizens were fish, cold-water river dolphins and alligators also cruised there. Dolphins were not a threat. Youngsters often played with them—much to the latter's annoyance—and, therefore, did not think of them as a prey species. Alligators were another matter altogether. They were prey to an adult dragon and predator to a youngster.

Thus, the dragoness took umbrage when she spotted the snout of an alligator lurking along the bank under the overhanging foliage. Almost completely submerged, it was inching its way toward one of her offspring. The youngster was distracted, chasing fish along the same bank. The dragoness rumbled sharply, alerting both offspring to become airborne immediately.

The predator reacted when the offspring nearest to it sprang from the water and into the air. It lunged at the youngster, raising its upper body out of the water. When it did so, the dragoness realized at once that it was not a native alligator. It was a huge crocodile with bizarre features—exaggerated fangs like those of a serpent, horns protruding from its skull, and a long, forked tongue that swept through the water (illustration 14).

The creature barely missed its mark. The dragoness did not. She snatched the creature in her powerful jaws, ending its life. Then, she shepherded her youngsters back to their den. They would have more lessons to learn from the River Della soon enough.

A Streamlined Physique

Freshwater dragons include river and lake species. The key differences between montane dragons and freshwater aquatic dragons are their size and preferred habitat. River dragons are sleek and slender.

Illustration 14: Varan

Like their arboreal cousins, river dragons feature smaller, slenderer frames and are far more flexible than their land-based cousins. They have the shape and flexibility akin to a river otter. Like land-based dragons, both species have wings for powered flight.

River dragons have a thick layer of lanugo under their scales. Their scales are composed primarily of keratin, a highly durable and waterproof protein. Thick scales on their sides and underbellies buffer the blows from rocks and other debris they may encounter, especially when traversing rapids. The scales on their backs are thinner, which helps decrease their weight. Unlike purely land-based species, their scales do not overlap. Similar to the *arcturus alba*, muscles under the skin contract to pull scales tightly together, thereby keeping water out. All these features allow river dragons to surf the rapids and still dive into a river's depths.

River dragons are streamlined for rapid speed. They traverse category V and VI rapids, which camouflage their passage. They are rarely seen—even by eagle-eyed scouts. Their movements mimic water over rapids, and their stripes help them blend into the crests of the waters. It is across these rapids where one might catch a glimpse.

A key characteristic is their electrosensitive "mustache" whiskers, which they use to find prey underwater. Like other dragon species, they have raptor-like vision, acute hearing, and a keen sense of smell above water.

The Sitka and the Griseo

There are two subspecies of river dragons: the *sitka* (illustration 15), a temperate-water dragon, and the *griseo*, a cold-water river dragon. Key differences between the *griseo* and the *sitka* include their range, temperature tolerance, and inclination to take flight. Although both can fly, the *griseo* often hunts for prey on land as well as in river waters. The *sitka* prefers to hunt aquatic species; however, it will not turn down a tasty morsel that comes too close to the water. Both species like to sun themselves from time to time.

Illustration 15: Sitka

The *sitka* is a warm-water subspecies of river dragon that is similar in appearance to the *griseo*—and likely closely related to it. It ranges from the lower River Della past its confluence with the River Lacus and through the mountain pass to just beyond the pass where they turn back. Although they prefer cooler waters, they tolerate warmer waters and may range as far south as the River Ferveo in search of food. The Ferveo's water temperature, however, is too warm for them to linger there.

The *griseo* is a cold-water subspecies of river dragon named for its grayish-blue color, except for a white dorsal stripe that travels from the top of its head to the tip of its tail and irregularly shaped white splotches on its back that lend the appearance of choppy white water. It patrols the northern portion of the River Della, running its category III and IV rapids with aplomb. Its stripe blends perfectly with the rapid's white water. This species prefers the cold waters flowing from the mountains.

Dark Waters

Except when traversing rapids or hunting land-based species, aquatic dragons require deep, wide rivers for concealment. Rivers must be at least 10 miles across and 200 feet deep, with large volumes of flow over a steep gradient. River dragons will turn back from shallower waters unless there is sufficient vegetation to provide cover and support an adequate food supply. Thus, their territory is limited primarily by water depth.

River dragons are rarely encountered by humans. Their dens are located underground. They will identify a rise near a waterway, excavate an underwater canal, and carve out a den above the waterline.

Although river dragons prefer to swim, they will become airborne if they encounter large chunks of fallen debris, waters that are too shallow, or channels with category V and VI rapids that are too narrow. They will not hesitate to take flight to catch their prey.

Just as some land-based species, such as the *arcturus alba*, often fish in fresh or marine waters, freshwater dragons occasionally hunt on land. Their diet consists primarily of fish, some reptiles, and other aquatic mammals. They also feed on other hapless lifeforms that fall into the river and cannot escape it.

A Romp in the Rapids

Although quite capable of flight, young adolescents liked to frolic in the rapidly flowing river waters where they had honed their swimming and fishing skills. They also raced each other to decide which one was the fastest. Older adolescents challenged the rapids, further honing their skills. They dodged outcroppings and surfed over and around rocks and boulders, many of which were hidden in white water. They rode whirlpools with reckless abandon, allowing eddies to toss them around like a rollercoaster (illustration 16). Compared to a romp in white water, flying was ho-hum.

Lake Dragons (Dragonis Fluminibus Lacus)

Few lakes are large enough to harbor a dragon. Those that are near human settlements are avoided. Those in high mountain ranges and in the arctic might be sufficiently remote; however, they are too cold for lake dragons. These lakes are fed by meltwater from glaciers, snowmelt, and snowstorms. Although arctic dragons are known to dive into subarctic waters to catch prey, the dive is fast and shallow, with their scales tightly closed to keep water out. Lakes associated with rivers are more likely to be frequented by aquatic river dragons.

Rare sightings of a dragon have occurred in the remote, landlocked Lacus Antigua Mare. It was once the bay of an ancient sea until it was cut off by volcanism. Over time, rain, winter snowfall, and small tributary streams converted it into a vast freshwater lake as large and as deep as an inland sea. Hence, the Lacus Antigua could accommodate one or more dragons.

Illustration 16: Sitka Dragon Cruising Rapids

Little is known about Lacus Antigua dragons. Like other dragon species, they are very reclusive, and sightings are rare. Spotted only in low light, none has been seen in daylight. Hence, a number of possibilities present themselves to wildlife biologists. Lake dragons could be nocturnal, semiaquatic, subterranean cave-dwelling, or any combination as long as they have access to the lake and access to air if inhabiting a flooded subterranean cavern system. No one has spotted these dragons getting in or out of the lake, nor have they been seen taking flight. Thus, biologists hypothesize that these dragons may be a new species of subterranean dragon with access to a large, submerged cavern with a water level lower than its ceiling. This would allow space for one or more dragons to inhabit it.

Based on obscure sightings, these dragons are estimated to be comparable in size and shape to their montane kin. Hence, many people believe that lake dragons are really great gray dragons that have opted to go for a swim and bathe in lakes with depths that accommodate their size. Although this is possible, biologists think it unlikely. First, great gray dragons are diurnal and do not shun daylight. Second, great gray dragons have difficulty becoming airborne from the ground. They are much too heavy to launch from water. They would first have to get back on land . . . somehow.

Supplemental Notes and Citations

Underwater Caves and Cavern Systems

The Sistema Sac Actun is an extensive system of underwater caves, caverns, and tunnels (Kambesis, and Coke, 2016). Although completely submerged, the system has access to the sea.

CHAPTER 14
Arboreal Dragons

Dragonenesis Dragonis Arboralis
A Narrow Escape

An arboreal dragon chick was almost ready to fledge. It sat on the edge of its nest, attempting to try out its wings. Unfortunately, the chick's perch simply did not allow sufficient room. So, using its talons, the chick decided to climb higher into the canopy, where the foliage was less dense. Finally, having reached a branch that extended into the open, the youngster failed to recognize that the branch was dead.

As the chick ventured out, it tested its wings by hopping along the length of the branch. It was trying to gain enough liftoff to hover over the branch. As it bounced up and down, the dead wood cracked, tossing the chick off and into the air.

Now began a desperate attempt to stay aloft. The chick lacked sufficient wing strength to fly or hover. As it fell, it cried out to its mother and any other dragon in the canopy. Fortunately, the canopy below the dead limb was dense. The chick landed on some intertwined sequoia branches and promptly became tangled in them. His struggle to get loose only made his situation worse.

Arboreal dragons were not the only species occupying the sequoia canopy. Many other animals lived there, including tree foxes, an abundant supply of squirrels and chipmunks, tree snakes, and other denizens. Bobcats, black bears, and wolverines climbed the trees in search of prey. When the dragon chick fell, nearby animals quickly fled—except for a tree snake.

An arboreal ambush predator, the snake's camouflage melded it into the canopy (illustration 17). It resembled an unusually large green tree python, embellished with the fangs and venom of a cobra. Capable of injecting or spraying its venom, this creature was a hybrid, genetically engineered to bring down almost any animal. It would lurk in a tree, hidden by the foliage, strike out, hold its unsuspecting prey in its coils, and then inject or spray it with venom. A dragon chick trapped in the foliage made a tempting—if unrealistic—meal.

Illustration 17: Moresistrurus

As the chick struggled to regain footing, the snake moved quickly lest its potential meal escape. Yet the snake was not the only predator who noted the disturbance. A martin, a small but voracious predator, was also attracted by the chick's movements. It was adept at climbing and racing through trees to catch its primary prey: squirrels, chipmunks, and birds.

The martin had detected the chick's rumbles. The snake had perceived the vibrations. Both targeted the source and made a beeline for it. As the two predators raced to reach their quarry, they ran into each other. Ever the opportunist, the snake snatched the martin in its jaws and wrapped its coils around its competitor—a far more suitable meal. Martins do not have scales.

In the midst of this drama, the dragon chick had disentangled itself. The youngster proceeded to climb safely back to its nest to try again another day.

Arboreal Dragons
An Ethereal Physique

Arboreal dragons (illustration 18) are somewhat slenderer than their nearest cousins, the river dragons. They are the only dragon species light enough to hover. They are twelve to fifteen feet tall at the shoulders when standing on all four legs. Their body length is fourteen to twenty feet. The head and neck add an additional four to six feet and the tail an additional ten to twelve feet. Their wingspan ranges from twenty-eight to thirty-two feet. They are armed with a bite force of 500 pounds per square inch and fire that reaches twenty to twenty-five feet.

Illustration 18: Arboreal Dragon

This species features ear tufts like those of the harpy eagle. They can angle their tufts up to 120 degrees. These characteristics give them an exquisite ability to sense even tiny fluctuations in wind force and direction. Arboreal dragons also have thicker lanugo, which provides not only additional warmth but also supports flight. Spreading their scales apart allows more lanugo to surface. This traps air, which provides more buoyancy, facilitates lift, and allows them to soar.

Similar in character to those of the red dragons, their scales are thinner and lighter. The scales on their ventral surface—the underside of their neck, belly, and tail—are a deep grayish-green with streaks of silver and blue. This coloration matches the appearance of the canopy with light streaming through the trees. The scales on their dorsal surface—the head, back, and top of the tail—are a deep reddish-brown, which helps them blend against tree trunks. Hence, their coloring camouflages them from the ground and from above. Their dark dorsal scales absorb light rather than reflect it, keeping them warm at high altitudes.

A streamlined body makes them agile, allowing them to traverse the canopy with ease. Their ability to compress their wings tightly against their body facilitates mobility. Powerful talons and claws grip tree limbs and trunks, and they use their tail for balance. Unlike other arboreal mammals, dragon tails are not prehensile.

Similar to other montane and freshwater aquatic dragons, arboreal dragons are omnivorous. Although they will eat fruits and nuts and nibble on cone seeds, they are primarily carnivorous.

The Sequourieae and the Pinaceae

There are two subspecies of arboreal dragons. Over millennia, a volcanic plain eroded and was subsequently colonized by vegetation and, ultimately, covered by interior forests. During the dragon migration, these forests became the home of two arboreal dragon species. Each subspecies is named for the trees they inhabit: the *arboralis sequourieae* and the *arboralis pinaceae.*

These two subspecies are essentially the same species except for their adaptations to a warmer versus colder climate. The *sequourieae* settled in a more southerly region, where the weather is temperate and sequoia redwoods grow. The *pinaceae* settled toward the north, where the temperature is cooler, winters can be harsh, and Douglas fir trees grow.

Forest Giants

Both species of trees are huge, not only in diameter but also in height, providing the sturdiness the arboreal dragons require. A giant sequoia can reach a height of 275 feet. Its trunk ranges from thirty to forty-five feet in diameter. Branches of the sequoia are the size of tree trunks in other tree species. Dense foliage begins about one half to two thirds of the way from the ground; however, the canopy gradually thins out toward the top, providing ample room for dragons to move through it. Thick, coarse, reddish-brown bark covers the trunk.

The Douglas fir's trunk is much smaller, with a diameter of eleven to twelve feet. Yet it is the taller of the two species, with an average height of 325 feet. The trees of both species are clustered close to each other. Branches overlap, forming a dense canopy all year round. Hence, little sunlight creeps onto the ground below. Light filters through only at the periphery during late morning and early afternoon.

Superb climbers, arboreal dragons can vanish into the foliage without taking flight. Although adults can squeeze their way through the canopy, they cannot fly through it. They are too large, and the foliage is far too dense. Youngsters learn early—sometimes by trial and error—to climb trees via branches that can bear their weight. They enjoy romping through the trees and over the canopy, demonstrating their agility. Once they become adolescents, however, they must use weight-bearing branches to traverse the trees. With the exception of newborn chicks, dragons use their talons and claws to ascend, descend, and navigate through the trees. Once they are below the branches, they often glide to the ground unless they are pursuing prey.

Just as gray and red dragons lift off from mountain crags, arboreal dragons become airborne by using a main branch near the top of a tree. They can quickly reach an altitude of 12,000 feet. They can also take off from the ground without difficulty.

When these dragons lie still in the canopy, they cannot be detected. They are nearly impossible to see until they take flight or ambush unwary prey on the ground. An astute and watchful scout can detect their presence when they are moving through the canopy. Huge tree limbs will sway, as if caught in a gale force wind. Yet the air is undisturbed, except perhaps for a slight breeze.

A Game of Chase

In a dense forest, arboreal chicks and youngsters were developing much-needed agility by playing tag through the canopy. These youngsters, including chicks not yet fledged, were small enough and slight enough to spread their wings and glide from one tree trunk to another. Then, in a game of chase, they would scramble up the trunk and back into the canopy.

Unfledged chicks learned quickly that if they landed on the ground, it would be a long climb back up. A chick on the ground had to be rescued quickly. Gray foxes, bobcats, black bears, and badgers inhabited the forest. Some of them could climb trees, and all of them preyed on dragon chicks. A hapless chick in distress need only utter a high-pitched rumble for help, and an adult or older adolescent would dive to the forest floor to retrieve the chick. Clambering onto its rescuer's back, the chick would hitch a ride back up to the canopy.

Supplemental Notes and Citations

Sequoias

Mature sequoias lack branches on the lower half of their trunks. Their bark may be two feet thick at the base, which protects the tree from fires. Each seed cone averages about 230 seeds. Most trees reach a height of 250–275 feet with a diameter of fifteen to twenty feet. The largest of these trees can reach a height of 310 feet with a diameter of thirty-five feet (Habeck, R. J. 1992; Van Pelt, R., 2001; Weatherspoon, C. P., n.d.).

CHAPTER 15

Subterranean Cave- and Cavern-Dwelling Dragons

A Ghostly Figure

A group of young people were hiking through a forested region adjacent to low-level foothills when, suddenly, one of them stumbled and fell to the ground. His outstretched arms broke his fall. His companions immediately drew around him.

"Are you alright?" asked one comrade.

"Did you hurt yourself?" queried another.

"I'm alright," replied the stumbler. "I stepped into a hole," he added.

Indeed, he had. As his comrades helped him to his feet, he described what he felt. "There is an empty space there. My foot just dangled freely."

"This may be a sinkhole," said a member guardedly. "We should move away from here in case the ground collapses, carrying us with it."

"Maybe there is a cave underneath," spoke another eagerly. "We could explore it."

Suddenly, the ground shuddered underneath them, followed by a shallow roll.

"Earthquake!" a member shouted.

"It is too shallow for an earthquake," remarked another.

The discussion became academic when the earth around the narrow hole fell away, enlarging it to four or five feet in diameter.

The troupe quickly jumped away and began a hasty retreat. With the hole enlarged, the activity subsided.

Gingerly, a few members inched their way back toward the sinkhole.

"It's a cave!" one called back excitedly.

"No," remarked the other. "It's a cavern. Listen to the echoes when the earth falls away. They take a long time to fade in the distance."

"Let's explore it," suggested a member of the group.

"We don't have the gear," said another.

Abruptly, the two members looking down into the hole jumped back, moving away as quickly as possible.

Speaking in a low whisper, one admonished, "Get behind those boulders! Stay still! Make no sound!"

The grayish-white, tapered head of a dragon appeared in the orifice. It had four long whiskers on its snout—two on either side. It rose to reveal a slender neck. The dragon had responded to the disturbance of the ground—perhaps a hapless prey was within easy reach.

The dragon's head swept around the edges of the sinkhole, surveying the immediate area with its whiskers. Although the dragon appeared to view the scene, to the group's surprise, it disregarded them. Their absolute stillness and silence served as camouflage against the sightless dragon. Sensing no prey, the dragon withdrew back into the sinkhole.

The group continued to remain silent and perfectly still. The dragon could still be lurking just below the surface. It was a long wait. Finally, with a nod to each other, the group slipped away and headed straight back to their village. They were eager to report a new dragon.

Cave-Dwelling Dragons

Many dragons often use caves as temporary retreats from weather conditions or as nesting sites. All three species of montane dragons occupy caves located high in the mountains. Solitary dragons, dragons who have left their clan to strike out on their own, or those who have yet to join a clan often occupy shallow caves in the mountain foothills. Like other montane dragons, they are diurnal and spend a good deal of time outside while hunting, surveilling the territory, and raising their offspring. In contrast, there are two species of subterranean cave- and cavern-dwelling dragons that live in deep recesses below ground. Rarely, if ever, do these species come above ground in daylight.

Subterranean Cave Dwellers: Dragonis Caverna Trogloxenos. A Muted Physique

The trogloxene species of cave-dwelling dragon is comparable to that of other land-based dragons. They are somewhat smaller than their red dragon cousins—an adaptation to living in a more constrained setting. Their scales are a dull, rusty gray color that does not reflect light, allowing them to blend in darkness.

Their vision is adapted to low light and darkness. Their retinae have an abundance of specialized receptors (rods) that enhance vision in a low-light environment. They also have infrared sensors to target prey in total darkness and rely on them to hunt other nocturnal species. These sensors are rendered inoperative in sunlight, leaving them virtually blind in full sun. Hence, they need to retreat deep into their cave where darkness hides them and their infrared sensors can spot any intruders.

Seclusion

This species lives almost exclusively in deep caves, where ambient light does not reach. They prefer caves that are largely underground with only a single egress that is carefully guarded. They are primarily a nocturnal species and very secretive. They retreat into the far recesses of their cave during broad daylight. They emerge after sunset to hunt, returning to their cave before sunrise. During periods of low light, they also conduct surveillance and teach their fledglings how to fly, hunt, and avoid predators.

Levitation

After killing a deer, a cougar dragged its prey just inside a cave, keeping a sharp eye out for any other predators that might try to steal its kill. After satisfying its hunger, the cougar climbed up a nearby tree for a postprandial snooze. The sound of movement abruptly aroused the cat. It saw its meal being dragged further inside the cave. The cougar promptly jumped down, seized its prize, and began to pull it back. Suddenly, the head of a trogloxene dragon appeared—its jaws open wide to engulf both the deer and the cougar. The latter levitated instantly, vaulted backward, and scrambled away—leaving the dragon with a bountiful feast.

Illustration 19: Subterranenan Cavern-dwelling dragon

Subterranean Cavern Dwellers: Dragonis Caverna Trogophilis
A Ghostly Physique

Troglophile dragons are the smallest known dragon species, with a slender body akin to a river dragon with similar features (illustration 19). Their scales have a scant, ghostly gray pigment. They have long whiskers with sensitive sensory hairs and use echolocation to identify family members and locate prey.

These dragons have enhanced auditory perception; however, they have minimal visual perception. Their retinae contain only enough rods to provide nominal visual acuity in the almost absolute darkness of a cavern system. It allows them to perceive bioluminescent prey (e.g., fish, glow worms, crustaceans, and the occasional shark), algae, and fungi. When exposed to direct light, an extra opaque membrane covers their eyes.

The wings on this species of dragon are vestigial. Hence, these dragons cannot fly. They use their wings to determine spatial parameters within the cavern system, including any river flowing through it. They have short back legs with dragon claws and longer forelegs with talons. They use their talons and claws to navigate across rocky surfaces and rely heavily on their tail to propel them through river systems. A bony crest on the top of the head alerts these dragons that a passageway is narrow.

Troglophile dragons generate electric currents via highly specialized nerve cells that conduct electrical impulses. These cells are aligned so an electrical impulse is transmitted when they are discharged. When cells are discharged simultaneously, the summation of all the electrical impulses generates a high-voltage electrical shock that is emitted in pulses. When discharged in sequence, they emit low voltage in a wave form. High-voltage pulses are emitted to stun or kill prey or an attacker. Low-voltage waves are emitted for communication and navigation.

The long whiskers of troglophile dragons are bioluminescent. They are used to attract unsuspecting prey looking for a meal of their own. Although their diet is primarily fish, they do not hesitate to feast on the occasional animal that falls into the cavern system. When food sources decline, they will rise to the surface on a moonless or heavily overcast night to catch unwary prey. Given the rarity of their appearance above ground, there is no lingering scent to alert an animal that it is passing a predator's lair.

Eternal Night

Troglophile dragons live exclusively in deep, complex subterranean cavern systems that have a freshwater source. Despite the total darkness of their environment, these dragons use their whiskers, wings, and bony crest to build a mental map of their cavern system. These cavern systems also have freshwater lakes and rivers coursing through them, some of which empty into the ocean. Troglophiles have taste and scent receptors that detect changes in salinity, which distinguishes a source of freshwater from saltwater.

Spelunking

Cave-dwelling dragons are well aware of humans and try to avoid them by retreating into darkness. Seasoned scouts readily recognize the charred walls of a dragon cave and prudently retreat. When they do so, there is no conflict between dragons and humans.

All dragons avoid cavern systems that were once inhabited by humans during *Stella Ignis*. Hence, these systems are well known to humans and carry only those risks associated with exploring them. Spelunkers who are eager for adventure and want to explore unknown cavern systems face a deadly hazard. To the troglophile species, humans are just another tasty mammal to have stumbled into their domain.

Supplemental Notes and Citations

Subterranean Species of Animals

There are three categories of cave- and cavern-dwelling animal species (Trajano and Carvalho, 2017). Trogloxenes (e.g., bats) live in caves and forage outside their caves. Troglophiles (e.g., some species of worms, salamanders) live primarily in the dark; however, they can survive above ground. They may have low vision (e.g., decreased visual acuity). Troglobites (e.g., some species of fish, shrimp, crayfish, salamanders) are animals that live exclusively in caves and caverns and are not exposed to sunlight. Many troglobites have no body pigment (albino) and may be blind or very light sensitive. They have highly sensitive sensory hairs and long antennae, which provide sensory perception.

Bioluminescence

Bioluminescence is the biologic ability of living organisms to emit light via biochemical reactions (Fleiss and Sarkisyan, 2019). It is a visual form of communication that may be used to attract a mate, tempt prey, or deter a predator.

Rods and Cones

Cones provide very high visual acuity, especially in daylight. Rods enhance visual acuity under very low levels of light, especially at night (Lamb, 2016).

CHAPTER 16

Marine and Brackish-Water Dragons

A Fresh Start

Many years after *Stella Ignis*, a large community of people migrated north *en masse* to a subarctic region. Seeking safety from the armed conflicts occurring in southern regions, they fled from a temperate climate to a less hospitable one. After establishing a settlement, which they named Gregor, immigrants began exploring their new environment. They identified many familiar plants and animals that had migrated there and adapted to the subarctic climate and terrain long before any humans had arrived.

Animals included a wide array of species, among them land mammals (e.g., arctic foxes, wolves, hares, bears), marine mammals (e.g., whales, seals, walrus), birds (e.g., snowy owls, terns, ptarmigans, and even a tundra swan), freshwater river fish (e.g., char, grayling), and marine fish (e.g., arctic cod). Even insects could be found seasonally. During the arctic spring, flowering plants bloomed (e.g., poppies, arctic lupine, Labrador tea, parraya). There were no native trees. Once the new settlement was well established, Norway spruce were introduced.

Marine Life

Initially, the settlers observed native wildlife species without engaging with them. This included the aloof arctic dragon that fished in both freshwater rivers and the ocean. Most marine life was readily visible and recognizable, even from shore. Beluga whales frolicked among the ice flows. Bowhead whales could be seen easily from the shore, as could seasonal humpback and gray whales. One unidentified species of whale stayed far out in the Arctic Ocean. Even at that distance, it could be readily seen. It was even larger than the bowhead, which was sixty feet long and weighed sixty tons. Once, when the unidentified whale was seen in a breach, it looked suspiciously like an enormous orca; however, it lacked the six-foot dorsal fin of an orca.

Although far from being seafaring mariners, nearly every settler had learned long ago how to navigate rivers and lakes using boats, kayaks, barges, and rafts. The settlers brought these skills with them. So, during the spring thaw, they would set out in kayaks or small boats to cruise these waterways, as they had done in the rivers and lakes of their former homeland. The beluga and humpback whales would often draw near to the boats and might cruise alongside them. It was a treat to be so close to these magnificent animals.

Still, it was prudent to stay a safe distance away. It would not do to be near a whale that suddenly decided to be frisky. Even so, it was thrilling to see such massive animals rise out of the water in a spectacular breach.

A New Species

One day, some would-be seafarers ventured farther out into the Arctic Ocean, hoping to observe one of the reclusive whales and, possibly, identify its species. They were not disappointed.

A huge bulge of seawater—like a sea swell—was sweeping across the ocean perpendicular to the boaters' heading. Something was moving rapidly through the water at roughly fifty miles per hour.

The boaters frantically started rowing backward, staying perpendicular to the swell's direction. Suddenly, the bulge ballooned as a marine mammal launched into the air in a breach (illustration 20). Seeing it rise out of the water, the boaters could clearly distinguish the head and long neck of a dragon, its modified wings, and the whip of its tail, as it provided additional power to vault the dragon into the air. Within the dragon's jaws was the body of an orca. Dinner had been served.

The swells generated by the dragon's pursuit of the orca and its breach hastened the shaken seafarers' return home. Once ashore, they recovered quickly. They were eager to report what they had witnessed.

Illustration 20: Odontoceti in breach

After the subarctic settlers had encountered their first sea dragon, they remained alert for other dragon species. Before immigrating to the subarctic, they had already encountered a variety of land-based dragons.

Marine Dragons: Dragonenesis Dragonis Oceanacertum

As a general rule, marine dragons are a predatory species. Though enormous in size, they are sleekly built for greater speed. They lack the forelegs that land-based dragons have, and they do not have flukes like whales. Their flippers are modified wings with characteristics of both, and their long tail serves as both rudder and whip. They have an exquisite sense of electroreception that allows them to target and catch prey underwater.

As mammals, they must breathe air, so they are obliged to surface periodically. They can stay submerged for up to two hours before resurfacing. All have salivary and incendiary glands to produce fire that is just as effective above water as that of any land-based dragon. Although they can use fire underwater, its power and distance are compromised.

Dragonensis Dragonis Odontoceti

The Odontoceti are by far the most dominate and far-ranging of the marine dragons (illustration 21). Known as the blue dragons, they are so named because of the deep-blue color of their scales, extending from the top of the head, over the back, and down the top of the tail. The underside scales are white. Streamlined for speed, they are the smallest of the marine dragons. At forty to forty-five feet long, they weigh 24,000 pounds (twelve tons). They are the dragon equivalent of an orca and roam throughout temperate and cold waters.

The Odontoceti have the characteristic head and neck of a dragon. Using their flippers and tail, they can achieve speeds of nearly fifty miles per hour (approximately forty-three knots) underwater. Although they have lost the ability of sustained flight, they can launch out of the water and over most fishing boats either in a breach or in an attack. They use their fire mostly above water.

Illustration 21: Odontoceti

Dragonis Glacialis Odontus Alba

Known as the white dragons, this species is resident throughout the arctic region. As a marine mammal, it is not related to the montane *arcturus alba*. The *odontus alba* is midsized at fifty to sixty-five feet long and weighs an estimated 32,000 pounds (sixteen tons). Its color is white-gray.

Subarctic settlers discovered this dragon when they observed it coming close to the pack ice. This species preys on sea otters, dolphins, sea lions, seals, and occasionally polar bears. Although they do not disturb the settlers' boats, the dragons' diet serves as a warning to those *H. transformans* whose alternate species happen to be this dragon's prey.

Dragonis Glacialis Balaenidae

Another resident throughout the arctic region, its color is dark gray. It also has an average length of fifty to sixty-five feet and weighs an estimated 28,000 pounds (fourteen tons). As a result, this dragon is often mistaken for the *odontus alba*.

The *Balaenidae* were misnamed. At first glance, they looked like filter feeders. In lieu of sawtooth-shaped teeth, they evolved with relatively straight, razor-sharp teeth, closely arrayed in both the upper and lower jaws. From a distance, the teeth look like baleen—a characteristic of filter feeders.

Dragonis Ballaena Caeruleum

This is a migratory species whose range extends from eastern to western oceans. They have a uniform blue-gray color. These dragons are filter feeders, relying on zooplankton. By far, they are the largest marine dragon at 80 to 112 feet long, weighing an estimated 92,000 pounds (forty-six tons).

An Ocean Frolic

Many of Gregor's subarctic human residents enjoyed whale watching—mostly for the rare opportunity to spot an ocean-faring dragon. The wildlife specialists kept a detailed record of dragon sightings. Over time, they recognized that the species *glacialis odontus alba* was a permanent resident. They also learned that *odontus alba* was the arctic equivalent of the *Odontoceti*.

Observers had to be extremely cautious since the *odontus alba* could launch itself onto the edge of pack ice to seize large prey. It did not consider small mammals—an arctic fox or snow hare—worth the effort. Fortunately, humans also seemed to fall into that category.

One day, a wildlife specialist observed an *odontus alba* cruising past the edge of an ice pack. It was looking for a suitable meal. As he moved a little closer, he noticed a hump on it.

Could this be a pregnant dragoness? he wondered.

Then the hump abruptly started moving past the presumed-pregnant dragoness, rapidly picking up speed. Suddenly, it launched itself almost completely out of the water in a breach. The "hump" was her baby, having a good time frolicking in the ocean.

Brackish-Water Dragon: Dragonis Odontus Pristis

The *Pristis* is a semi-marine species of dragon that favors brackish waters (illustration 22). It is a resident species of swamps and estuaries. Often referred to as a swamp dragon, it is the only aquatic dragon that can also swim in marine waters. Even so, it is not a strong swimmer and must remain close to the coastline.

Illustration 22: Odontis pristis

Pristis is twenty-eight to thirty-six feet long and weighs 16,000–22,000 pounds (eight to eleven tons). Its dark bluish-black color camouflages it both in swamps and open water conditions. With a long, narrow head, a tapered snout, and razor-like upper and lower teeth, it is consistent with other predatory species. Its eyes glow with a green color, courtesy of its tapetum lucidum. Its forelimbs have partially webbed feet and sharp talons. Like the arctic dragon, when submerged, it folds its wings tightly against its body and uses its forelimbs and tail to propel itself. Relatively slender hind limbs extend behind the animal when it is in the water, yet they allow the dragon to walk on land. A long tail serves as a rudder, propeller, and weapon and also provides balance in an upright position on land. *Pristis* can reach speeds of thirty to thirty-five miles per hour in the water and can hold its breath underwater for thirty to forty minutes.

Although the *Pristis* is diurnal, it is largely a nocturnal predator. Its eyes have a high ratio of rods to cones, which improve its visual acuity at night. In addition, it can detect infrared (IR) radiation via specialized IR sensory organs below each eye. This allows the dragon to form IR images of warm-blooded animals. Thus, vision and IR imaging are complimentary systems that support the identification and targeting of multiple prey species. *Pristis* preys on both swamp and marine wildlife—and any other species that wanders into its domain.

Supplemental Notes and Citations.

Electroreception in Fish

Sharks and eels are species of fish that use electricity to hunt prey and for self-defense (Bellono, *et al.*, 2018; Catania, 2019). Sharks have electrosensory organs that detect electric signals from prey species. The electric eel generates low-voltage and high-voltage impulses. Low-voltage impulses are primarily for communication and navigation, whereas high voltage is used to disable or kill prey.

Native Whales

The blue whale is the largest known whale at seventy-five to eighty feet long, weighing 290,000–330,000 pounds (145–165 tons).

The fin whale is the second largest whale at sixty-four to sixty-six feet long, weighing 100,000 pounds (fifty to seventy-five tons).

The bowhead whale is sixty feet long, weighing 120,000 pounds (sixty tons).

The right whale is forty-five feet long, weighing 100,000–150,000 pounds (fifty tons).

The sperm whale is fifty to fifty-two feet long, weighing 90,000 pounds (forty-five tons).

The orca (killer whale) is approximately thirty feet long, weighing 8,000–16,000 pounds (four to eight tons), and can reach speeds up to twenty-eight miles per hour.

EPILOGUE
Unexpected Encounters

A high rocky ledge overhanging an escarpment finally gave in to gravity. It broke away, falling down a steep slope and carrying a fledgling dragon with it. It broke into chunks of rock as it tumbled down into a forested region below. The fledgling was snared in the debris—unable to escape it and unable to fly out of danger. It called out to its mother as it fell. The debris finally crashed into the forest, carrying the fledgling with it as it settled among the trees.

A human scout witnessed the entire event, including the fledgling's fall. He had to run from the flying debris himself. With no parent nearby to aid the young dragon, the scout ran back to the debris field to check on the fledgling. At first, the scout thought the chick was dead. It was lying limp, not moving. Nevertheless, he began removing debris to get a better look and detected that the youngster was breathing. The scout began in earnest to remove as much debris as possible. Unfortunately, some pieces were too large and too heavy to move. He couldn't even budge them.

Suddenly, the scout saw a huge talon reach from behind him. He froze. Intent on rescuing the young dragon, the scout had not heard its mother coming up behind him. She moved around him to pick up a large slab with her talon and set it aside. Then she grasped another heavy rock in her jaws and tossed it away.

The scout was amazed. He had rarely seen dragons from a distance. Now a massive dragoness was right beside him, dwarfing him. For a moment, he continued to watch as the dragoness removed one huge block after another. Then the scout resumed picking up and tossing aside pieces that he could handle. Between the two of them, they finally cleared the debris around the young dragon.

The scout watched as the dragoness sniffed and nudged her baby. It did not respond. The dragoness's head blocked a clear view, so the scout could not tell if the young dragon was still breathing. The dragoness picked up the youngster's limp body in her talon, took several brisk steps across the debris field, and flew away. The scout could only hope that the young dragon had survived the fall.

A Tacit Understanding

Some dragon clans became friendly with humans. Most, however, remained aloof. Yet, one community of humans developed a strong relationship with some clans of red and great gray dragons. Known as H'Aletheans, these people occupied the territory that abutted the southwest mountains—the domain of the red dragons. H'Alethean territory extended northward into the montane forest. The northwestern branch of their territory, known by them as Caput Canis (the Dog's Head), encompassed a small part of the forest (illustration 23).

The forest stretched northward and into the foothills of the northern mountain range. This region bordered two other communities—the Biogenics Corporation and the Cassius Foundation—each of which claimed territories of their own and were archrivals. Armed conflict frequently broke out between the two. These battles often spilled into H'Alethean territory to their south. The great gray dragons had witnessed armies of humans and bizarre creatures battle for dominance. Hence, they kept a close watch on human activities while making every effort to avoid any contact with them.

Encounters with the human species proved to be inevitable. Both dragons and humans—with many hunters among the latter—traversed these territories, along with a host of other animals. It seemed as though humans thought they were the dominant species of the land—a misapprehension that some dragons wished to correct. Prudence prevailed as long as the two species kept their distance.

Yet random chance precluded the segregation of humans and dragons. The ambitions of the Cassius Foundation drove its desire to acquire dragon DNA. So, it sent bounty hunters to kill dragon youngsters and steal dragon eggs. Although hunter-dragon encounters were rare, they served as a reminder that danger was ever present. Even dragons had to be wary.

Still, not all humans threatened the welfare of the dragon species. The H'Aletheans actively tried to protect the red dragons for fear the latter would be hunted into extinction. (As the dominant species, the dragons recognized the irony of this notion.) Thus, over time, both parties developed a tacit uderstanding to live and let live.

Illustration 23: Map of Territories

ACKNOWLEDGMENTS

I wish to express my gratitude to Mrs. Suzanne Smith Sundburg, BA, Phi Beta Kappa, for her expertise as a copyeditor, and to Ms. Esther Ferington for her expertise as a developmental editor. I also wish to acknowledge Mr. Ross Cuippa, art director, and Carl Cleanthes, creative director, and the graphic artists and illustrators of EpicMade who provided the dramatic scenes and vivid renderings of dragons featured in the narrative.

GLOSSARY

Adaptive changes—normal physiologic changes that enhance functionality and/or prevent loss of function.

Amniotes—species whose embryos are enclosed by an amniotic sac (mammals, birds, and reptiles).

Analogous—having similar structure and function via a different evolutionary ancestor (e.g., mammalian hair follicles are analogous to avian feather follicles).

Biologic classification system (taxonomy)—kingdom, phylum, class, order, family, genus, and species.

Bioluminescence—the physiologic ability to glow in living organisms.

Clade—a group of organisms that include all descendants with a common ancestor. Birds, dinosaurs, and crocodiles all have a common egg-laying ancestor.

Cladogram—schematic demonstrating the evolutionary lineage of a species.

Class (taxonomy)—a group of organisms that have a common genetic background yet are genetically distinct from each other and thus have similar but distinct physical characteristics (e.g., mammals). Bacteria, reptiles, fish, dinosaurs, insects, mammals, birds, etc., all represent different classes within the animal kingdom.

Common ancestor—two or more different species descending from the same ancestor.

Conservation of genes—genes that provide a survival advantage or are essential to life are passed on to subsequent generations.

Crown group—a group comprised of all species that share a common ancestor, both living and extinct.

DNA—deoxyribonucleic acid, structural material that holds genetic information.

Echolocation—ability to locate and possibly identify objects by emitting and receiving sound waves.

Electroreception—detection of electric fields caused by muscle contractions.

Endonuclease—an enzyme that can cut out a damaged DNA gene and repair the strand.

Endothermy—maintenance of a relatively constant body temperature by metabolic means.

Energy metabolism—a cascade of biochemical reactions that converts glucose into energy (in the form of adenosine triphosphate, ATP) which is used as fuel for cellular processes.

Epidermis—outer layer of skin. The outermost layer of skin, the stratum corneum, consist of layers of dead keratin cells (keratinocytes).

Epigenetic effect—nongenetic influence (e.g., environment, methyl groups) on the expression of a gene.

Eukaryotic cells—cells that contain specialized organelles not found in more primitive organisms (prokaryotes), including a nucleus in which DNA is organized as chromosomes.

Eutriconodont—an order of early mammals that continued to evolve into modern orders of mammals (e.g., primates).

Family (taxonomy)—species that fall into the same class yet are still genetically distinct.

Genes—a set of three constituents (nucleosides) that form the basic building blocks of DNA. Coding genes determine the physical component used in building a biologic structure (e.g., a protein). Noncoding genes regulate function of other genes.

Genetic adaptation—changes in genetic composition that allows an individual to adapt to his/her environment.

Genome—the total gene compliment of an individual organism.

Genotype—an individual's overall genetic composition whether or not it is expressed as an observable characteristic.

Genus (taxonomy)—groups of species whose genomes are very similar yet remain distinct: e.g., the genus Homo includes the species *H. habitus, H. erectus, H. neanderthalensis,* and *H. sapiens.*

Homologous—having the same or similar structure and function derived from a common ancestor (e.g., genetic homology).

Homeothermic—ability to regulate and maintain a stable internal body temperature via metabolism, independent of environmental temperature (thermoregulation).

Invertebrates—animals without a bony skeleton—specifically, lacking a backbone.

Isthmus—a narrow land bridge, formed by tectonic activity or made of sand, linking two land masses that otherwise would be separated by the sea.

Language—usually associated with meaningful combinations of words or sounds.

Mammary (milk) glands—specialized glands in female mammals that produce milk for the young (e.g., breasts or teats).

Metabolic pathway—a sequence of biochemical reactions leading to a biologic outcome (e.g., energy production).

Middle ear bones (ossicles)—the malleus (hammer), incus (anvil), and stapes (stirrup).

Monotreme (prototheria)—oldest mammals that lay eggs to produce their young (e.g., duck-billed platypus, spiny anteater).

Oviparous—eggs are developed outside the mother's body and offspring hatch from the eggs.

Ovoviviparous—eggs are incubated until they hatch, after which the mother gives birth.

Phenotype—an individual's observable manifestations (physical characteristics) of genetic composition.

Radiation—ionizing radiation (e.g., X-rays, gamma rays) can induce genetic changes including gene mutations and chromosomal rearrangements.

Species—any group of organisms that is genetically similar yet maintains a distinctive set of genetic and physical characteristics.

Stem ancestor—ancestor at the base of a branch.

Taxonomy—in biology, a hierarchical organization wherein plants, animals, and other forms of life are grouped according to their physical characteristics and, more recently, on genetic analysis. The farther down the hierarchy an organism falls, the more closely related it is to other similar life forms.

Troglobites—animals that live in caves and caverns.

Troglophiles—animals that live primarily in the dark yet can survive above ground.

Trogloxenes—animals that live in caves and forage outside caves.

Ultrasound—sound emitted at a frequency above the level of normal human hearing.

Vertebrates—animals with a bony skeleton—specifically, one having a backbone (vertebral column).

REFERENCES

Preface

Jones, K. E., and Safi, K. (2011). Ecology and evolution of mammalian biodiversity. *Phil. Trans. R. Soc. B*, 366, 2451–2461. doi:10.1098/rstb.2011.0090.

Vavrek, M. J. (2016). The fragmentation of Pangaea and Mesozoic terrestrial vertebrate biodiversity. *Biol. Lett*, 12, 20160528. http://dx.doi.org/10.1098/rsbl.2016.0528.

Veevers, J. J. (2004). Gondwanaland from 650–500 Ma assembly through 320 Ma merger in Pangea to 185–100 Ma breakup: supercontinental tectonics via stratigraphy and radiometric dating. *Earth-Science Reviews*, 68, 1-132. https://doi.org/10.1016/j.earscirev.2004.05.002.

Prologue

Jönsson, K. I. (2019). Radiation Tolerance in Tardigrades: Current Knowledge and Potential Applications in Medicine. *Cancers*, 11, 1333.

Ishino, S., and Ishino, Y. (2014). DNA polymerases as useful reagents for biotechnology - the history of developmental research in the field. *Frontiers in microbiology*, *5*, 465. https://doi.org/10.3389/fmicb.2014.00465.

Paul, B., and Montoya, G. (2020). CRISPR-Cas12a: Functional overview and applications. *Biomedical Journal*, *43*(1), 8–17. https://doi.org/10.1016/j.bj.2019.10.005.

Prelude

Carbonaro, T. M., Bradstreet, M. P., Barrett, *et al.* (2016). Survey study of challenging experiences after ingesting psilocybin mushrooms: Acute and enduring positive and negative consequences. *J. Psychopharmacology (Oxford, England)*, *30*(12), 1268–1278. https://doi.org/10.1177/0269881116662634.

Madsen, M. K., Fisher, P. M., Birmester. D., et al. (2019). Psychedelic effects of psilocybin correlate with serotonin 2A receptor occupancy and plasma psilocin levels. *Neuropsychopharmacology*, 44, 1328–1334. https://doi.org/10.1038/s41386-019-0324-9.

Tylš, F., Páleníček, T., & Horáček, J. (2014). Psilocybin--summary of knowledge and new perspectives. *European neuropsychopharmacology: Journal European College of Neuropsychopharmacology*, *24*(3), 342–356.

PART I. EVOLUTION & MIGRATION

Chapter 1. Of Dinosaurs and Dragons

Bacon, C.D., Silvestro, D., Jaramillo,C., *et al.* (2015). Biological evidence supports an early and complex emergence of the Isthmus of Panama. PNAS May 12, 2015 112 (19) 6110-6115. https://doi.org/10.1073/pnas.1423853112.

Davis, C. C., Bell, C. D., Mathews, S., *et al.* (2002). Gondwanan disjunctions: Evidence from *Malpighiaceae. Proc Natl Acad Sci U S A*, 99(10), 6833-6837. doi: 10.1073/pnas.102175899.

Egbert G. Leigh, Aaron O'Dea, Geerat J. Vermeij (2014). Historical biogeography of the Isthmus of Panama. *Biological Reviews*, 89(1), 148-172. https://doi.org/10.1111/brv.12048.

Fiorillo, A.R., McCarthy, P.J., Kobayashi, Y. *et al.* (2018). An unusual association of hadrosaur and therizinosaur tracks within Late Cretaceous rocks of Denali National Park, Alaska. *Sci Rep* 8, 11706. https://doi.org/10.1038/s41598-018-30110-8.

Flannery, T.S., Archer, M., Rich, T.N., Jones, R. (1995). A new family of monotremes from the Cretaceous of Australia. *Nature*, 377, 418-420 (letter).

Gavrilov-Zimin I. A. (2021). Egg retention, viviparity and ovoviviparity in Paraneoptera. *Comparative cytogenetics, 15*(3), 239–252. https://doi.org/10.3897/CompCytogen.v15i3.70216.

Kielan-Jaworowska, Z. (1992). Interrelationships of Mesozoic Mammals. *Historical Biology*, 6, 185-205.

O'Dea, A., Lessios, H. A. Coates, A. G., *et al.* (2016). Formation of the Isthmus of Panama. *Sci Adv*, 2(8), e1600883.

Turner, A. H., Makovicky, P. J., Norell, M. A. (2007). Feather Quill Knobs in the Dinosaur Velociraptor. *Science*, 317, 1721.

Weisbecker, V., and Beck, R. M. D. (2015). Marsupial and monotreme evolution and biogeography (Chapter 1). In: A. Klieve, L. Hogan, S. Johnston, P. Murray (eds.), *Marsupials and Monotremes*. Nova Science Publishers. ISBN: 978-1-63482-973-1.

Chapter 2. Dragon Evolution

Anderson, S. C., and Ruxton, G. D. (2020). The evolution of flight in bats: a novel hypothesis. *Mammal Review*, 50(4), 426-439.

Bergmiller, T., Ackermann, M., & Silander, O. K. (2012). Patterns of evolutionary conservation of essential genes correlate with their compensability. *PLoS genetics*, *8*(6), e1002803. https://doi.org/10.1371/journal.pgen.1002803.

Cooper, K. L., and Tabin, C. J. (2008.). Understanding of bat wing evolution takes flight. *Genes & Development*, 22, 121-124.

Deakin, J. E. (2017). Implications of monotreme and marsupial chromosome evolution on sex determination and differentiation. *Gen Comp Endocrinol.* 244, 130-138. doi: 10.1016/j.ygcen.2015.09.029.

Flannery, T.S., Archer, M., Rich, T.N., Jones, R. (1995). A new family of monotremes from the Cretaceous of Australia. *Nature*, 377, 418-420 (letter).

Hu, Y., Meng, J., Wang, Y., Li, C. (2001). Large Mesozoic mammals fed on young dinosaurs. *Nature,* 433, 149-152.

Ilango, S., Paital, B., Jayachandran, P., Padma, P. R., & Nirmaladevi, R. (2020). Epigenetic alterations in cancer. *Frontiers in bioscience (Landmark edition)*, *25*(6), 1058–1109. https://doi.org/10.2741/4847.

Jones, K. E., and Safi, K. (2011). Ecology and evolution of mammalian biodiversity. *Phil. Trans. R. Soc. B*, 366, 2451–2461. doi:10.1098/rstb.2011.0090.

Kielan-Jaworowska, Z. (1992). Interrelationships of Mesozoic Mammals. *Historical Biology*, 6, 185-205.

Koina, E., Fong, J., Graves, J. A. (2006). Marsupial and monotreme genomes. *Genome Dyn*, 2, 111-22. doi: 10.1159/000095099.

Luo, Z-X. (2007).Transformation and diversification in early mammal evolution. *Nature*, 450 (13), 1011-1019. doi: 10.1038/nature06377.

Maul, S., Giegling, I., Fabbri, C., *et al.* (2020). Genetics of resilience: Implications from genome-wide association studies and candidate genes of the stress response system in posttraumatic stress disorder and depression. *Amer Journal Medical Genetics. Part B, Neuropsychiatric Genetics,* 183(2), 77–94. https://doi.org/10.1002/ajmg.b.32763.

van Leeuwen, J., Pons, C., Boone, C., Andrews, B. J. (2017). Mechanisms of suppression: The wiring of genetic resilience. *BioEssays: News and Reviews in Molecular, Cellular and Developmental Biology, 39*(7), 10.1002/bies.201700042. https://doi.org/10.1002/bies.201700042.

Zheng, W., Guo, J., & Liu, Z. S. (2021). Effects of metabolic memory on inflammation and fibrosis associated with diabetic kidney disease: an epigenetic perspective. *Clinical epigenetics, 13*(1), 87. https://doi.org/10.1186/s13148-021-01079-5.

PART II: FORM & FUNCTION

Chapter 3. To All Appearances

Chen, I. H., Kiang, J. H., Correa, V., *et al.* (2011). Armadillo armor: mechanical testing and micro-structural evaluation. *J Mech Behav Biomed Mater*, 4(5), 713-22. doi: 10.1016/j.jmbbm.2010.12.013.

Choo, S. W., Rayko, M., Tan, T. K., *et al.* (2016). Pangolin genomes and the evolution of mammalian scales and immunity. *Genome research, 26*(10), 1312–1322. https://doi.org/10.1101/gr.203521.115.

Einoder, L., and Richardson, A. (2006). An ecomorphological study of the raptorial digital tendon locking mechanism. *Ibis,* 148, 515–525. (doi:10.1111/j.1474-919X.2006.00541.x).

Simandl, G. (2009). Structure and function of the skin. In: Porth, C. M., and Matfin (eds), *Pathophysiology: Concepts of Altered Health States* (8th ed.), Chapter 60. Lippincott Williams and Wilkins.

Wang, B., Yang, W., McKittrick, J., Meyers, M. A. (2016). Keratin: Structure, mechanical properties, occurrence in biological organisms, and efforts at bioinspiration. *Progress In Materials Science*, 6, 229-318.

Yang, W., Chen, I. H., Gludovatz, B., *et al.* (2013). Natural flexible dermal armor. *Adv Mater*, 25(1), 31-48. doi: 10.1002/adma.201202713.

Chapter 4. Fire and Flight

No references.

Chapter 5. A Quarry's Scent

Au, W. W. L., & & Simmons, J. A. (2007). Echolocation in Dolphins and Bats. *Phys. Today,* 60(9), 40. doi: 10.1063/1.2784683.

Czech-Damal, N. U., Dehnhardt, G., Manger, P., & Hanke, W. (2013). Passive electroreception in aquatic mammals. *Journal of comparative physiology. A, Neuroethology, sensory, neural, and behavioral physiology, 199*(6), 555–563. https://doi.org/10.1007/s00359-012-0780-8.

Han, J., Waddington, G., Adams, R., *et al.* (2016). Assessing proprioception: A critical review of methods. *Journal of sport and health science, 5*(1), 80–90. https://doi.org/10.1016/j.jshs.2014.10.004.

Lambert, M. J., Nevue, A. A., Portfors, C.V. (2017). Contrasting patterns of adaptive sequence convergence among echolocating mammals. *Gene,* 605, 1-4. doi: 10.1016/j.gene.2016.12.017.

Manger, P. R., and Pettigrew, J. D. (1995). Electroreception and the feeding behavior of platypus (*Ornithorhynchus anatinus*: Monotremata: Mammalia). *Phil Trans R. Soc. Lond. B,* 347, 359-381.

Renaldi, A. (2007). The scent of life. *EMBO reports,* 8(7), 629-633.

Thaler, L., Arnott, S. R., Goodale, M. A. (2010.) Human Echolocation I. *J. of Vision,* 10(7), 1050. doi: https://doi.org/10.1167/10.7.1050.

Chapter 6. Decision-Making

Nair, S., *and* Balakrishnan, R. (2009). Vocalizations of wild Asian elephants (*Elephas maximus*): Structural classification and social context. Journal of the Acoustical Society of America, 126 (2768). doi: 10.1121/1.3224717.

Stoeger, A. S., Heilmann, G., Zeppelzauer, M., *et al.* (2012). Visualizing Sound Emission of Elephant Vocalizations: Evidence for Two Rumble Production Types. *PLoS One*, 7(11), e48907. doi: 10.1371/journal.pone.0048907.

Chapter 7. The Passing of a Patriarch

Bozek, K., Khrameeva, E. E., Reznick, J., *et al.* (2017). Lipidome determinants of maximal lifespan in mammals. *Scientific reports*, *7*(1), 5. doi:10.1038/s41598-017-00037-7.

Calnan, D. R., Brunet, A. (2008.) The FoxO Code. *Oncogene*, 27(16), 2276-88. doi: 10.1038/onc.2008.21.

Edwards, J. E., Hiltz E., Broel, F. (2019.) Advancing Research for the Management of Long-Lived Species: A Case Study on the Greenland Shark. *Front. Mar. Sci.*, https://doi.org/10.3389/fmars.2019.00087.

Hammon, H. M., Liermann, W., Frieten, D., & Koch, C. (2020). Review: Importance of colostrum supply and milk feeding intensity on gastrointestinal and systemic development in calves. *Animal: an international journal of animal bioscience*, *14*(S1), s133–s143. https://doi.org/10.1017/S1751731119003148.

Keane, M., Semeiks, J., Andrew E., *et al.* (2015). Insights into the Evolution of Longevity from the Bowhead Whale Genome, *Cell Reports*, 10(1), 112-122. https://doi.org/10.1016/j.celrep.2014.12.008.

Kessler, E. C., Bruckmaier, R. M., Gross, J. J. (2020). Colostrum composition and immunoglobulin G content in dairy and dual-purpose cattle breeds. *Journal of animal science, 98*(8), skaa237. https://doi.org/10.1093/jas/skaa237.

Kim, S. Y., Yi, D. Y. (2020). Components of human breast milk: from macronutrient to microbiome and microRNA. *Clinical and experimental pediatrics, 63*(8), 301–309. https://doi.org/10.3345/cep.2020.00059.

Mayne, B., Berry, O., Davies, C. *et al.* (2019). A genomic predictor of lifespan in vertebrates. *Sci Rep* **9,** 17866. https://doi.org/10.1038/s41598-019-54447-w.

Montero-Serra, I., Linares, C., Doak, D. F., *et al.* (2018). Strong linkages between depth, longevity and demographic stability across marine sessile species.

Quesada, V., Freitas-Rodríguez, S., Miller, J., *et al.* (2019). Giant tortoise genomes provide insights into longevity and age-related disease. *Nat Ecol Evol,* 3(1), 87–95. doi:10.1038/s41559-018-0733-x.

Vaiserman, A. M., Koliada, A. K., & Jirtle, R. L. (2017). Non-genomic transmission of longevity between generations: potential mechanisms and evidence across species. *Epigenetics & chromatin, 10*(1), 38. doi:10.1186/s13072-017-0145-1.

PART III. HEARTH AND HOME

Chapter 8. Territories

Giuggioli, L., Potts, J. R., Harris, S. (2011). Animal interactions and the emergence of territoriality. *PLoS Computational Biology, 7*(3), e1002008. https://doi.org/10.1371/journal.pcbi.1002008.

Potts, J. R., & Lewis, M. A. (2014). How do animal territories form and change? Lessons from 20 years of mechanistic modelling. *Proceedings. Biological sciences*, *281*(1784), 20140231. https://doi.org/10.1098/rspb.2014.0231.

Schmidt, M. H., Stears, K., Shrader, A. M. (2016). Zebra reduce predation risk in mixed-species herds by eavesdropping on cues from giraffe. *Behavioral Ecology*, 27(4), doi:10.1093/beheco/arw015.

Chapter 9. Hunting

No references.

Chapter 10. Reproduction

Renfree, M. B., Hore, T. A., Shaw, G., *et al.* (2009.) Evolution of Genomic Imprinting: Insights from Marsupials and Monotremes. *Annual Review of Genomics and Human Genetics*, 10, 241-262. https://doi.org/10.1146/annurev-genom-082908-150026.

Chapter 11. Raising Offspring

No references.

PART IV. THERE BE DRAGONS

Chapter 12. Montane Dragons

No references.

Chapter 13. Freshwater Aquatic Dragons

Kambesis, P., & Coke, J., G. (2016). The Sac Actun System, Quintana Roo, Mexico. *Boletín Geológico y Minero*, 127(1):177-192.

Chapter 14. Arboreal Dragons

Habeck, R. J. 1992. *Sequoiadendron giganteum.* In: Fire Effects Information System, [Online]. U.S. Department of Agriculture, Forest Service, Rocky Mountain Research Station, Fire Sciences Laboratory (Producer). https://www.fs.fed.us/database/feis/plants/tree/seqgig/all.html.

Van Pelt, R. (2001). *Forest Giants of the Pacific Coast.* Global Forest Society in collaboration with University of Washington Press, Seattle.

Weatherspoon, C. P. (No date.) *Sequoiadendron giganteum* (Lindl.) Buchholz. https://www.srs.fs.usda.gov/pubs/misc/ag_654/volume_1/sequoiadendron/giganteum.htm.

Chapter 15. Subterranean Dragons

Fleiss, A., and Sarkisyan, K. S. (2019). A brief review of bioluminescent systems. *Current Genetics,* 65, 877–882. https://doi.org/10.1007/s00294-019-00951-5.

Lamb, T. D. (2016). Why rods and cones?. *Eye (London, England)*, *30*(2), 179–185. https://doi.org/10.1038/eye.2015.236.

Trajano, E., and Carvalho, M. R. (2017). Towards a biologically meaningful classification of subterranean organisms: a critical analysis of the Schiner-Racovitza system from a historical perspective, difficulties of its application and implications for conservation. *Subterranean Biology*, 22: 1-26. https://doi.org/10.3897/subtbiol.22.9759.

Chapter 16. Marine and Brackish Water Dragons

Bellono, N. W., Leitch, D. B., & Julius, D. (2018). Molecular tuning of electroreception in sharks and skates. *Nature*, *558*(7708), 122–126. https://doi.org/10.1038/s41586-018-0160-9.

Catania, K. C. (2019). The Astonishing Behavior of Electric Eels. *Frontiers in integrative neuroscience*, 13, 23. https://doi.org/10.3389/fnint.2019.00023.

Epilogue

No references.

Milton Keynes UK
Ingram Content Group UK Ltd.
UKHW012102300823
427795UK00002B/6